UNCHARTED
CONSTELLATIONS

Edited by

Siobhan Logan and Darragh Logan-Davies

Space Cat Press

Table of Contents

Preface

When we dreamed up this anthology back in 2019, the world was commemorating the fiftieth anniversary of the first lunar landings and reflecting on humanity's journey towards becoming a space-faring species. By the time those Apollo 11 astronauts planted their 'Stars and Stripes' in the moon-dust, the Sixties' Space Race had transformed modern culture in ways no-one could have predicted. Today, various superpowers and private companies are competing in a second Space Race to found lunar colonies and send crewed missions to Mars. And, once again, such leaps in technological advancement are inspiring creative minds to conjure up their own journeys among the stars. With this anthology, we wanted to see how writers in the twenty-first century perceive space exploration. Sifting through the submissions, we noted several recurring themes emerging.

In the *Moon Warriors* section, our authors delve into the notion of heroism implicit in the Moon Race legend. Tom Wolfe famously captured the gendered nature of NASA's programme by describing the Apollo astronauts as having 'The Right Stuff'. James Worrad's eerie flash fiction flips around that machismo in a wonderfully unexpected way. Then poems by Emma Lee and Deborah Tyler-Bennett touch on the less glamorous reality of life back on Earth for prominent Russian and American astronauts. By contrast, stories by Rob Bray and Richard Urwin see two different protagonists inspired by the same historical event realise new possibilities for themselves. James Walton's Australian desert poem rounds the section off by conjuring up an idyllic landscape infused with haunting reminders of those first moon walks.

The pieces in the next section, *Worlds Beyond*, begin to contemplate humanity's place among the stars. J.K. Fulton's sci-fi story follows generations of scientists as they investigate otherworldly rocks during a century of meteorological encounters. Similarly Rod Duncan's 'hermit crab essay' focuses on a fascination with comet-watching being passed from father to son. Several poems in this section explore the relationship of the Moon's alien body to planet Earth: Kathleen Bell's mournful dreamscape contrasts with Mark Goodwin's whimsical personal reflections. Then Michele Witthaus questions the perceived calm of the 'ball of frosted blue' photographed by Apollo astronauts from the lunar surface. Pushing deeper into space, James Walton's flash fiction unfolds a lyrical fable of space colonisation while Simon Fung's female explorer braves a weird voyage through an alien underworld in pursuit of sentient life.

The Space Race once looked to be an exclusively white-male narrative. But in our *Star Women* section, writers have countered that failure of imagination with wit and awe. Teika Marija Smits conjures up a young lady inspired by female astronomers and radicals of the Wollstonecraft era. Despite her comment that 'it seemed as though women were everywhere, doing everything', it would take far longer than it should have for women to travel to the stars. Even when America's Mercury 13 women aced their gruelling space testing regime, NASA refused to send them to the stars. For two decades, the Soviet textile worker Valentina Tereshkova remained the lone star in the records of space women. Valentina appears in Mary Byrne's story as a kind stranger who encourages the teenage protagonist to pursue what makes her happy, instead of doing as she was told. Meanwhile in Katherine Franklin's exhilarating *Pathfinder* story, the fate of the world depends on an elderly Indian woman who embarks on a one-way mission to locate a new home for humanity. Her ultimate sacrifice in this story echoes Laika's fate, as unpicked in Sarah Doyle's poem. By contrast, Emma Lee's 'What became of the girl who counted' celebrates another groundbreaking Space Woman: Katherine Johnson, a gifted mathematician whose one star observation system brought the Apollo 13 crew back to Earth safely.

Many of these pieces capture that sense of breaking free of both social and physical barriers. However, there are notes of dissonance throughout the anthology which come to the fore in our *Dystopian Skies* section. Tim Bombdog's poem, 'The Chequered Flag', has a deliciously satirical streak that challenges NASA's Stars and Stripes propaganda. Meanwhile

James Walton's poem juxtaposes Alexei Leonev's perilous space walk with his father's experience of being exiled to a Stalinist gulag. Prisoners also star in J.K. Fulton's *Always Carry A Spare*, a space adventure fueled by pitch-black humour with life-or-death stakes. There's a gentler tone to Yevgeny Salisbury's flash fiction but it too has dark undertones, featuring self-aware androids in no rush to have their human masters join them on their promising new world. Humanity is also viewed with some disdain by the moon goddess of Rebekah Tobias' 'Hue of Blue' poem. And then we finish with Paul Rudman's disturbing sci-fi tale, *Mother*, where hallucinations will be the least of your concerns...

MOON

WARRIORS

The man from NASA arrived the next morning. Walter Igwe met him at the crash site out beyond the maize fields. Walter found the man's handshake overly firm.

'The agency,' the NASA man said, 'would like to thank you, Mr. Igwe. For the quick response.' His temples ran slick with sweat. He clearly wasn't used to such sun and, doubtless, would catch his return flight long before he acclimatised.

'It was nothing, sir,' Walter replied. 'Really. My whole town offers the agency our condolences.'

'Appreciated, Mr. Igwe.' The man brushed an insect from his nose. 'But it's just a setback. Ultimately I mean.' He laughed. 'Albeit an expensive one.'

Walter hid his disgust. Was nothing sacred in America? A man was dead. *Their* man.

'The main section,' Walter told him, 'the, er, capsule, is over there.'

They made their way over the scorched ground. Seeing the blackened capsule again, Walter remembered pulling the body out from its torn shell. His spacesuit had been perfectly white. Walter had half-believed the astronaut still lived. Yet the visor was smashed and behind it lay burnt flesh and bare teeth. It had taken all Walter's strength to drag the corpse from that cramped space.

The NASA man spent the next two hours cataloguing every piece of wreckage. He would look at some burnt mechanism and mutter 'Write off', then move on to the next. Walter said nothing but his hands were fists.

'You'll come to our town now?' he asked the NASA man after he'd finished his inspection.

'I'd love to, really,' the man replied, 'but they expect me back at the capital.'

'But he's there now,' Walter said, doing his best to stay civil. 'Our refrigerators are all too small so we have wrapped him.'

The other man's brow crumpled. 'I ... don't get you.'

'Damn it, sir!' Walter snapped. 'Your man, your astronaut! He died for you! For your mission!' He wanted to slap the man's face, to remove that blank expression. 'A death is not a setback! It is not an expense!'

'But, Mr. Igwe...' The NASA man gestured at the wreckage. 'This is a satellite. It's unmanned.'

The two men stared at one another. Save for the hum of insects, the world fell silent.

One Small Step

Rob Bray

21st July 1969

He raced down the concrete steps, took a giant leap onto the tarmac apron in front of the flats. Then he ran, rubbing his face, her cloying scent still in his nostrils. Only when he reached the dark emptiness of the park did he slow and begin to pick his way through leafy pathways into a tidier, more prosperous area of the town. His panic subsided as he took a shortcut through the spinney, the round white moon bright in the sky, the beech shadows dark, solid. It was way after midnight, but the night was warm. He walked under the dark fringe of trees. Behind him, a car hissed along the main road. At the bottom of his street, one house, un-curtained, was bathed in blue.

Beyond the gravelled drive, Mrs. Sutherland's large Victorian house sat in darkness. He'd lodged here for almost six months while he pursued his mission to complete his doctorate. In spite of their differences – she, a refined Scottish widow and he, a thrifty student of archaeology – the arrangement had worked well.

He slid his key into the lock, inched the door open. At the foot of the stairs he stopped, heard strange, distorted words and static coming from the small TV room. He turned the door handle slowly, pushed.

Mrs. Sutherland sat, legs tucked up, in a round upholstered chair, her grey hair in its usual tight bun. On a small table at her side a silver tray held tumblers, a bottle of whiskey and a jug of water. Her handsome, angular face was turned towards the television in the corner of the room. In her lap, she cradled a half-filled glass.

He looked at her, then his attention switched to the small screen and its grey, shifting and ghostly images. The soundtrack a crackling commentary punctuated by sharp bleeps. Without taking her eyes from the screen, Mrs. Sutherland reached across and patted the chair on the other side of the table.

'Good timing. Seven minutes to landing.'

Her voice, low Morningside, was warm. He let his bag slide from his shoulders, sat, brushed a hand over his hair. The screen was filled by a pale, curved disc, pock-marked. The image overlaid with blurred data. Time to landing. Altitude. Speed. Mrs. Sutherland raised her glass to her lips, sipped. He shifted in his chair, tried to make sense of the technical language. Gave up.

'The moon's bright,' he said, 'clear. Amazing to imagine them, up there.'

She glanced at him, smiled. Turned back to the screen. He learned forward, elbows on his knees, concentrating. The time to landing ticked down, altitude slipped to thirty thousand feet. The pock-marked surface of the moon slid by. Mrs. Sutherland sipped again.

'Sarah rang. Three times.'

The moon's surface grew nearer, the pock-marked craters clearer. He sat straighter.

'I'm sorry,' he said. 'I asked her not to.'

The numbers on the screen were tumbling quickly, the craters looming larger.

'My God,' said Mrs. Sutherland.

He braced himself. Mrs. Sutherland leaned forward, her glass held in both hands.

'They're aiming for a particular place,' she said. 'I told her you were working. She said she'd already called the bar.'

Her fine profile was tinged by flickering blue light. The image on the screen seemed to tremble and dissolve. She raised her glass again. He closed his eyes, slumped in the chair, raised his hands in submission.

'I must've left before she rang. I'm sorry you've been dragged into this. I thought she'd...'

The image on screen changed abruptly. Now it showed blurred, angular shapes, the static worsened. Mrs. Sutherland tilted her head, frowning.

'Is that part of the … what's it called, the landing module?'

'I expect so. I did ask her to wait until I…'

She raised a palm. From the tinny television speaker came a clear sentence.

'Houston. Tranquillity Base here. The Eagle has landed.'

Mrs. Sutherland turned to him, eyes wide. A voice, less distorted by static, cut in.

'Tranquillity. We copy you on the ground. You got a bunch of guys about to turn blue. We're breathing again.'

'My God,' she said. 'They've done it! They're on the moon!'

They looked at each other, looked back at the screen.

'Astonishing,' he said, 'miraculous.'

The TV image changed to a group of men in white shirts and ties hunched over desks and banks of screens.

'It's hard,' said a voice, 'to convey the pride and the concentration felt in this room at this moment. At this point, vital checks and close scrutiny of all systems must be carried out and we'll now take you back through the momentous events of this day and, as soon as we can, we'll return to live transmission from the moon.'

More men talking, more grainy shots of crowds and the towering rocket gantry, men carrying what looked like suitcases moving in procession along scaffolded walkways. Mrs. Sutherland leaned forward, turned the volume down.

'How long do you think it will be before we see them walking on the moon?'

'Some time, perhaps. They'll need to be painstakingly careful. They'll have list after list of procedures, checks.'

'Yes, though I'd envisaged them leaping out of their spaceship, doing the soft shoe shuffle!'

She looked at him.

'She sounded upset. Confused. Wanted to talk. I said I was the wrong person, only you could help her.'

Holding his breath, he shook his head. She waited a beat then turned back to the screen. He made himself exhale.

'I'm sorry you were bothered.'

Her eyes flicked to the screen and back to him, one hand pushed the bottle across the table him. He topped up his whisky with water as she'd taught him, swallowed a mouthful.

'It's become very complicated,' he said. 'She's distressed.'

'You don't have to say anything. It's your business.'

She turned back to the silent screen.

'I don't know where to begin,' he said.

'If you don't, who does?' she said and leaned forward. The picture had jumped to a jumble of blurred grey shapes. 'What's that?' said Mrs. Sutherland.

'A ladder?' he said, 'someone descending, perhaps.'

A sharp intake of breath. 'My God, you're right, quick, the sound.'

This time, he knelt and turned the knob.

The ghostly images shifted, a crackly voice cut through the static.

'That's one small step for man, one giant leap for mankind.'

They looked at each other. Mrs. Sutherland's eyes were alight.

'What did he say?'

She turned back to the screen, glass to her lips. They watched as the shimmering shape of a man, distorted by a huge encumbrance on his back, slid awkwardly and in slow motion across the screen.

He held his glass tight against his chin. Seconds, moments, passed.

'It's a Monday night in the middle of England,' he said, 'and we're watching men, walking on the moon, right now. It's incredible.' He heard the wonder in his voice.

Mrs. Sutherland raised a hand, her eyes never leaving the screen. The image had clarified into a misshapen figure. The images flickered, the commentary fell silent. They watched together, in their ears the deep, regular ticking of the clock on the mantlepiece.

'I don't think I can be what she wants me to be,' he said, 'or live how she wants to live. Everything mapped out, planned in advance. Everything. It suffocates me.'

'Plans matter,' she said without taking her eyes from the screen. 'Imagine the planning behind this. Someone devised those lists.'

When he didn't respond she turned to face him. 'I've met her only once, when you first arrived. I liked her. You shouldn't hurt her unless you have to.'

He rolled his glass between his palms.

'I know that.' he said, 'Look, there's two of them.'

On the screen two shapes, more clearly human, in spite of round fish bowl heads, were moving slowly, rocking, stepping backwards before leaning forwards and stepping off again. Their words, edged with static and abrupt bleeps, were clear enough.

'It's comfortable, natural ... you've to lean in the direction you want to go, get your feet right under you.'

'That's it,' he said, 'What I want. To be comfortable, natural, my feet right under me. Into the future, whatever happens.'

Mrs. Sutherland looked at him. The whisky burned his throat.

'She's updated her lists,' he said. 'Plates, cutlery, napkins, side plates, serving spoons. Asked me what I thought about condiment sets. I've been avoiding her all day, ignoring her calls.' He paused, swallowed. He wouldn't mention going off with the barmaid after his shift. He tasted again the cheap wine they'd drunk, wondered if Mrs. Sutherland could smell her on him.

The two shapes had clustered together under the skeletal umbrella of their craft.

'Life support consumables looking good,' said a calm voice.

Mrs. Sutherland turned from the screen, raised an eyebrow at him.

Now the image was lighter, in better focus. One of the shapes seemed to be pressing something against an angled strut. The crackling voice returned, its emotionless tone explaining that the spacemen were fixing a plaque to the space craft, it bore signatures and a message.

'We come in peace from all mankind.'

'And I thought they just wanted to beat the Russians,' he said.

She looked at him over the rim of her glass, pursed her lips.

He felt himself colour. On the grey screen the two figures had moved away, one was doing something with what looked like a pole, jabbing it into the surface. The other seemed to be half assisting, half unwrapping something.

'My God, an American flag!' said Mrs. Sutherland and threw him a quick glance. 'All right, you don't need to comment!'

He blew out his cheeks.

'Her father has offered me a job. Graduate trainee. No need to finish my PhD. My existing research skills will be enough. We'll be able to buy a house. Sarah's been to see a new development. She's very keen.'

Mrs. Sutherland looked at him for a moment. They sipped in unison, he stretched out his leg. She touched her hair.

'But I've been offered something else. Leading a dig on the Orkneys. Money not worth having, wooden shack for accommodation. Prospects nil.'

'Awkward.' said Mrs. Sutherland. 'I could understand if Sarah's not keen. She'll need new lists.'

He looked across at her, sharply, couldn't read her expression.

'I haven't told her,' he said.

A voice was instructing the astronauts to stand together in the camera's sight. They obeyed, hopping stiff-legged into position. The voice of the American President filled the room, Mrs. Sutherland made a quiet tutting sound, flapped her hand at the screen and twisted towards him on her chair, regarded him intently.

'Those two men are a quarter of a million miles away walking on the moon. Sarah is not so distant and needs to speak to you. You just have to take a dozen steps into the hall, ring her and explain what you want to do with your life and ask her to share it with you. It's 1969, I'm sure she'll tell you whether she wants to. Or not.'

Her gaze didn't waver. He looked away. When he looked back she'd turned back to the screen.

'It's the middle of the night,' he said. She waved a hand in dismissal.

On the screen, the men were moving across the pock-marked surface, small puffs of dust rose at their feet, one of them seemed to be dragging something on the end of a stick. They watched in silence. A louder voice intoned lists of numbers. Minutes passed

'Whatever they're doing now,' said Mrs. Sutherland, 'looks rather dull.'

'They're collecting soil and rock samples,' he said, 'setting up other experiments. Solar wind. Directed by scientists.'

'They look like they're litter picking,' she said.

When he looked at her, she'd wrapped her arms about herself and her mouth was drawn down in displeasure.

The voice-over was explaining the dangerous process of reuniting the lunar module with the circling command module. Mrs. Sutherland's expression didn't soften.

'I didn't have you down as a feminist,' he said.

Her profile when she turned to him in the soft lamplight was imperious.

'What did you have me down as? A list maker?'

He raised his hands in submission.

'No, not that, but...' He made a half-hearted gesture at the wood panelled room.

11

On the screen one of the moon walkers was at the base of the ladder. As they watched, his shadowy bulk rose up and merged with the structure of the module. The other was nowhere to be seen, instead, the screen was filled with view of the lunar module alone in front of the grey-white spread of the moon.

She reached for the bottle, poured, turned and offered it to him.

'My husband was the list maker. Milestones to wealth and success. Only one he failed to tick off, living long enough to enjoy it.'

She sipped, frowned at the screen. He poured himself a small glass, topped it up with water.

'I looked out of the window, saw him slumped over a tree stump. The tree which he'd cut down, lay across the lawn. We'd argued. I wanted to keep the tree, to buy others.'

Her face was set, shuttered.

'Afterwards, as you've seen, I bought a whole copse.'

The light from the TV changed, a man's face filled the screen, he spoke earnestly, drew diagrams on a board, explained the path of the lunar module towards its reunion with the Columbia command module.

'There's no margin for error,' said the man.

'There's always margin for error,' said Mrs. Sutherland. 'That's what life is.' When she smiled at him he could only nod. She raised her glass again. 'Now we'll be on tenterhooks to make sure they actually get off the moon alive.'

She turned back to the screen with her whisky. He sat there for a time, watching with her. More diagrams, more images of the moon's surface, of the skeletal lunar module shimmering, its hatches closed. Then, the oak floor creaking under his footsteps, he walked to the door. In the cool hallway, on the side table, the green telephone.

When he came back into the room, Mrs. Sutherland hadn't moved. On the screen, a different man held two models in his hands, manoeuvring them to show how the two-space craft would re-engage.

'I wouldn't like to be the other one,' she said, 'alone, worrying in case something goes wrong and they can't re-engage.'

They stared, without speaking, at the image of the lunar module, sitting ghostly on the moon's surface. He sat, his heart still jumping, hands gripped tightly between his knees, blood ticking at his temple.

'Tranquillity Base. Beautiful desolation,' Mrs. Sutherland said. 'Imagine being stranded there, forsaken.'

She turned, her face softened by shadow. He took a breath.

'I told Sarah about the post on Orkney, that I was going to take it. I very much hoped she'd come with me, but I was going anyway.'

Through hiss of static, came a small voice. 'Hatches closed and latched.'

'She's taken her mother's car, she's on her way here, probably orbiting the ring road right now. Whether to end our engagement or to throw herself into my arms, I don't know.'

The lunar module sat and glowed, it's undercarriage golden. Beside it, the flag stuck straight out.

'You're good to go,' said Huston.

'Understand, we're number one on the runway.' said a distorted voice, followed by a series of commands and responses.

'Fourth stage reset.'

'Earth control auto.'

Mrs. Sutherland, looked at him, fingers on her mouth.

'Pre-ignition checks,' he said.

Her eyes widened further. She crossed her fingers.

'Eagle, you're looking good.'

Mrs. Sutherland reached across, grasped his wrist tightly as the countdown began.

'Please God,' she murmured.

And then it was done.

'Very smooth, very quiet,' said a metallic voice interspersed with bleeps.

The moon's surface receded. Mrs. Sutherland released him. They looked at each other. The TV, abandoned, popped and stuttered with static and unintelligible words. Then she stood, smoothed down her skirt, looked down at him.

'How long until she...'

'An hour,' he said, 'just over.'

She nodded, kept her hands on her thighs.

'In which case,' she said, 'I'm going to change your bed linen, put fresh towels in your bathroom.'

'You don't need to do that.'

'Yes,' she said, 'I do.'

Awkwardly, he stood and faced her. Her smile was warm.

'One small step for a man,' she said. 'I'll leave the whisky.'

He stared at the flickering screen, the spectral shape of the landing module alone in the blanched landscape, the flag at an angle now, imagined the debris they'd left behind, their fallen boots, cameras, backpacks. Thought of the other one orbiting the moon alone, waiting.

What they were hired to do

Emma Lee

(21st July 1969, Armstrong and Aldrin landed on the moon. Michael
Collins remained in orbit in Columbia)

The man who travelled furthest is the one forgotten.
Left on Columbia, he was pulled behind the moon,
out of communication, thinking about returning alone.

The man left on Columbia sweated over engine failures
as he waited to hear whether they'd crashed back or risen
from the lunar surface where the lander had never been tested.

A speech was prepared in case Armstrong and Aldrin
failed to make the Eagle fire and stayed moon-bound.
Armstrong became a recluse, Aldrin battled addiction.

The third astronaut shunned fame. The moon's done.
He looks forward to Mars. *Heroes abound,*
but don't count astronauts among them, he said.

Yuri Gagarin in Dublin

Deborah Tyler-Bennett

For Martyn

Close by St. Stephen's Green – I dream the strangest dream,
Gagarin dancing at The Zanzibar.
Then Bewley's, through a morning coffee's steam
pale face blossoming, a dying star.
Lime afternoons by Patrick Kavanagh's
statue, he sits, coldly contemplates
soft ground beneath small feet (too shrunk by far
for spanning galaxies). His future grates,
beckoning desk jobs slam like closing gates.
It seems some dreams take on reality,
Gagarin dropped in Dublin by the fates:
hinting of earth-tied man's mortality;
a brackish Liffey plashes behind eyes
spilling planets as dull waters rise.

Waning Earth

Richard Urwin

Friday July 19th, 2069

'Not all of us have a family buggy, Nell,' Colin said.

'And even if we did, no way our parents could take time off on Eagle Day,' Ed said.

It was a kilometre from the habitat to school along a tunnel lined with mooncrete. They all had pushbikes, and then somehow ended up pushing them instead of riding. There were three of them: Nelly, a gawky blonde, twelve years old already and standing a head taller than her eleven year old companions; Ed, broad and dark; and Colin, small for his age with hair too red to avoid being called ginger.

'Tranquility Base is where it all started,' Nelly said. 'Armstrong and Aldrin, one small step for a man. Tomorrow it will be surrounded by news crews and scientists; it won't be real anymore.'

'Today,' said Colin, 'we're late for class.'

Nelly glanced at her mobi, swore under her breath and scooted her bike into motion, standing on one pedal. 'See you at break, guys.'

Ed looked at Colin and rolled his eyes. 'She thinks everyone has a billionaire father.'

***

'I agree with Nell,' Ed said. 'We should go to Tranquility before the scientists move in.'

Colin looked up from his lunch. 'We should, but no way we'd fit in Nell's buggy.'

Nelly shook her head. 'Two seats, two umbilicals.'

'I'll race you,' Ed said. 'The TV starts at eight. I'll be there.' He turned and left in the direction of the food bar.

Colin's lunch turned to lead in his stomach as he watched him go. The swagger was a dead give-away; Ed had found a way.

'Are ... are you coming too?' Nelly asked.

She wasn't being mean. She was never mean. She wanted him there. But all she had to do was smile at her dad. Ed would do something stupid and get into trouble. Colin obeyed the rules, never got into trouble and never had any fun.

'To wipe that smug grin off his face, I'd walk.'

Except that was one way that would never work. Tranquility was just too far. But if Ed had found a way, then he could too.

'How?' Nelly asked.

The siren saved him. Both of them opened their satchels, removed the flattened helmets and pulled them over their heads. The transparent plastic clung to his face. Breathing was impossible until the ring clicked into place against the neck of his suit. The helmet inflated. Nelly was still fiddling with her seal as he fished the rubber gloves out of his satchel. He plugged his umbilical into the wall socket. His suit had half-finished the self-test by the time Nelly plugged in beside him.

'Damn hair,' she said. 'I'm going straight to the barber after school and to hell with what Mom says.'

Colin nodded supportively. Nelly's mother spent less than half her time on the Moon. Everyone else knew that painful death was only a few metres of mooncrete away. The first colonists had worked in shirt-sleeves because the spacesuits of the time were too bulky but people had died. These smart suits were almost as easy to wear as jeans and a long-sleeved T-shirt. Colin had never worn anything else for as far back as he remembered. But they only worked if you could get the helmet on quickly. Long hair was fine but vacuum didn't care what you looked like.

His suit relaxed and the siren changed to the all-clear. Everyone repacked their satchels.

'I'll see you at Tranquility, Nell,' Colin said and beat a retreat before she could ask how.

***

It was 4 a.m. UTC when Colin reached the train station. The lights on the platform were dim, representing night-time. Outside it was dark too; the sun wouldn't rise for another three days. The media teams had set up tall floodlights at Tranquility Base so that they could record the erection of the gantries on Eagle Day. The darkness would make Colin's journey more difficult but he'd brought a torch and at least he didn't have to go outside.

Ed had found that the train – full of equipment, scientists and media teams – would leave the station at 7 a.m., and get to Tranquility Base half an hour later. There would be no way to get a seat on it but he could stow away. He'd get into trouble when they found him of course but by then it would be too late. Colin could do the same thing but he'd probably get caught and spoil it for both of them.

The lights along the rails were green. Colin had heard there were green lights but he'd never seen them before. Every time he had used a train the lights had always been red. The railways shut down at midnight and the maintenance teams worked from midnight until 6 am before the first trains at 7 a.m. So the track would be unpowered for two more hours. He'd have plenty of time to reach the station at Tranquility Base and be suited up ready to make his way over the surface. He couldn't know when Nelly would get there but her father wouldn't get up much before 6 a.m. She'd be there at eight for the news teams as they had agreed.

Colin lowered his bike over the edge of the platform and scrambled down after it. He could argue that there was no rule against riding along the tracks. He would probably get told off even so. The tunnel was lit only by the dim green lights. He mounted the bike and put his mobi in the handlebar cradle switched to GPS mode. Then he pushed off into the tunnel.

19

A white light appeared in the distance. Colin stopped under it. There was an airtight door in the wall of the tunnel. He could see a mooncrete wall through its window. It must be an emergency refuge in case the tunnel was depressurised. They would be at intervals along the track, near enough together for someone to reach one on emergency air. He pushed off again, wobbled slightly and came close to a rail. Careful; if he busted the bike he would never get there on time.

Privacy was rare in the colony. In bed or even on the toilet, there was always someone a few metres away. One never even needed to raise one's voice to be heard. Now Colin could shout and scream until he was hoarse and nobody would hear. He had never noticed the muted rumble of bike tires before. Now that was all he could hear. The world was green. The regular white lights seemed purple in comparison. He could barely see the walls around him, just a misty presence. Only the floor between the rails was clear, lit in mottled shades, first from one side and then the other. Sometimes it seemed that he, the floor and the tracks were standing still and the lights were the only things moving.

***

An hour passed. This was the furthest Colin had every ridden and there was a dull ache in his thighs. His vision flashed red for an instant. At first he thought the endless monotony was making his eyes go strange but then it happened again, a red flash. The green lights were turning red; a warning before the power came on. There was a white-purple light ahead. If he could reach that he could get into the refuge. Then he would have to call his parents. It wasn't a conversation he was looking forward to. By the time Colin reached the door the lights were as often red as green. Colin stumbled into the refuge, put the bike against the wall and pushed the door closed. He was in pitch darkness.

He fished the torch out of his pocket and turned it on. This wasn't a refuge; it was another tunnel, barely a metre wide. It didn't feel like a public area but there were no signs to say he wasn't allowed in here. The

20

race was not lost yet. He mounted the bike and held the torch against the handlebars.

After another hour, the tunnel ended at an airtight door. Behind it was another. There were three life-support packs standing against the wall. Colin pushed the bike to the far door and looked through the window. He saw a mooncrete ramp and black sky. A metal-walled tube carried the train out onto the surface. The GPS said he had less than five kilometres to go. So near and yet so far. If he reached Tranquility Base, then he could ride the train home and only have to deal with his parents. If he stayed here they would have to stop the trains and send someone after him.

***

The bike's wheels sank only a centimetre into the packed dust. Pedalling was harder than usual but not that difficult. It was so silent that Colin's ears felt numb but the view was spectacular. He'd never been out at night before. With no sun to hide them, the stars shone like tiny jewels and overhead the gibbous Earth hung, wispy white and deep blue.

Colin freewheeled to a halt, panting. There was a steep hill in front of him, all broken rocks and loose dust. There was no way he could climb it, much less ride the bike up it. The train tunnel went straight through but there was no maintenance access. Colin checked the map on his GPS. It was the wall of a crater, only a few hundred metres wide. The train line ran right through the middle of the crater and out the other side. He would have to go around. It only added another kilometre to the journey. Keeping half an eye on the map he turned the bike away from the train tunnel and followed the crater wall.

Colin rounded the side of the crater and set out across the open ground. It was faster that way than to rejoin the train line; the station was half a kilometre east of Tranquility Base. There was nothing around him but gently rolling terrain and the occasional boulder. He was absolutely alone.

The torch went out.

Colin took his hand off the handlebars to shake it. The bike hit a rock and he came down hard on his side. Damn, that was stupid. He lay there for a minute, listening for the hiss of air over the hammering of his heart. There was silence and the lights on his neck ring remained green, thank God. He struggled to his feet. Now he would have to call to be rescued; there was no way he could carry on in the dark.

Except it wasn't dark.

He could still see. The Earth was not as bright as daylight and it was too dim to ride the bike, but it was enough to see his way if he walked. He checked his mobi. Only two kilometres. He'd take it slow to be safe; he didn't want to fall again.

***

There was a fence. Just a single line of rope between widely spaced uprights. Seventy-five metres away, he could see the squat shape of the descent stage and beside it the American flag. He could hear their voices in his memories, see their grainy images superimposed on the greys and golds in the distance. The train was arriving at the station. Soon the media and the scientists would be here. Sightseers would wander around gantries over it all. It would be ancient history, pickled and preserved, and never the same.

A dozen or more figures came over a low rise to the east. They would be the media teams and the engineers. The buggies and trailers would be loading up behind them. Colin's solitude was over; he was rather sad to see it go. He hoped that he could convince them that he was supposed to be here. He rather doubted it though; he was probably going to be sent straight home in disgrace.

Two figures broke away from the crowd and bounded toward him waving wildly. Nelly's flashy suit with its pink trim was unmistakable even in the dim Earthlight. Of course her father would have been on the train. That must be Ed beside her. Colin grinned and waved back.

22

This time, all three of them had made it.

Neil Armstrong's Three Stage Punctuation

James Walton

In the slow orbit of wombats
my house hangs on to the hill,
the yellow frog flaunts the leaping crimson spinnaker of its jump
to the swallows' rue at my reflective door,
white lightning shudders in lift off from another unscheduled
countdown.

Wind dies.

Apple blossom carries the love letter kiss of butterflies,
delivered in the slow somersault breeze
moon landing clumsy, on the creek now river.
Stars tumble into it, where the eyes of my people well at the eddy;
dreams caught wanting the release of gentle hands not fossicking.

Later, on the plain before Narrandera:

Sun and moon stare it out on the flat,
through moving windows, I make no ground in their yellow orange disregard.
Rise and set, clocking on and off.
They know the contraband in my head is safe,
no small step can approach it.

WORLDS
BEYOND

Visible spectrum
Michele Witthaus

That swirling ball of frosted blue,
viewed over a mild grey horizon:
what kind of a message to the world was that?
Surely napalm, burning barricades
and the spilt blood of activists
should have hurled a lurid prism into space?
Yet Earth kept its blue distance.

Imagine the colours of an Earthrise today:
you'd expect bushfire, charred rainforest,
at the very least, a smashed kaleidoscope of plastic;
but even these hues would remain unseen
by another generation
in love with the fiction
of that blameless blue.

A short history of a universe in fold theory.

James Walton

Cater is sixth generation. The first messages took six months. It is now two hours. They are close. All droning work finished; the machinery locked away in the preservation bay. The maintenance schedule has its own pace, a litany of processes now closer to manual control. The most interesting event is the daily air reading, closer to life than ever. Not that she has been outside.

The library dome has been completely restored. It was fractured in generation three, before the atmosphere was thick enough to absorb the debris of the outer ring. Cater too has absorbed it all, the writings and stories of her once world. Her ancestors are shuffled in the dock behind, a keepsake for when the arrival occurs. Everything known, will be known again.

She is the last of the keepers. It is knowledge which neither scares or excites. It is the way, and the generations have worked their time, unpacking the first modules, the reappraisal of various sites, the preparation of each location, construction and repair. In decreasing numbers, each century reached the target stages, mapped and terraformed, built cities and gardens. They prepared basins for oceans, raised mountains, and seeded landscapes.

Now oxygen is outside as well as within. She is sometimes drawn to the labyrinth.

Stacked in the honeycomb are the first and the last of before. The hexagons rise and spread in an inverted pyramid of captured moments. Within each carapace a slow beat is monitored, measured, charged, regulated while decades irresistibly pass.

It is one second to alarm. The two suns have nuanced shades. The fleet hang-glides through the final year, propulsion and speed handed over to a calculated gravity. The geometry of descent marked through each intercession and passing through of pulsing circumferences.

Cater is unsurprised to see herself and feel her hand salute itself in the upper forearm grip. Except for the smile, which repeats on her face as well.

You are Cater, the Caretaker.

You are Ari, the Arrival.

Cater is neither scared or excited. She is the preparation and the waiting.

Ari is neither scared or excited. She is the journey and the beginning.

Earth Voyage 2019_Nos 3, 2, & 1
Mark Goodwin

Earth Voyage 2019_No 3

pincer

thumb & index
finger to

night sky

grip

the pill of
the moon

Earth Voyage 2019_No 2

if you
are fifty

like me we

all

began as
our night

sky's

bright round bone broke

our world's
waters

Earth Voyage 2019_No 1

moon pulls
our world's

liquids so

so

so

our time's
tides

        step

        and

        will

        leap

On the Path of Comets

Rod Duncan

Standing outside the back door in dressing gown and pyjamas, sleep clearing, I wonder why they woke me. My older brother looks up, bounces on his toes. Our father crouches and points to a place in the sky. Shifting closer to sight along his arm, I feel the warmth of him. There is a silvery line among the stars.

'It's a comet,' he says. 'On a journey from the icy cold.'

Comet. A new word.

'The tail is dust and gas,' my brother tells me.

Feeling their excitement, I know I should be sharing it.

'Where's it going?' I ask.

***

I'm with friends on the university campus, behind a bank of pine trees, shielded from the town's lights. In the field of my binoculars I find a grey mass without tail or clear edge. Hardly the fiery omen of the Bayeux Tapestry. But I've learned my father's thrill at such faint evidences. Here is a remnant from the formation of the solar system. A recurrent visitor, Halley's Comet is of the type they call short-period. I'll be a hundred next time it comes around. I hope we'll get a better display, and that my eyes will be up to it.

***

It is July 1994. A string of mountains in space are closing on Jupiter at thirty-seven miles a second. They will detonate just over the horizon from our earthbound view, each impact many times hotter than the surface of the Sun. The gas giant's rotation will quickly bring any damage into view and Hubble will see it all.

We wait by the television, my father and I, impatient for the first image to be released. And there it is: the impact marked by a dark spot in the swirling atmosphere. A journey of more than four billion years is done.

***

It is 2014. The Philae Lander approaches a barbell of ice and dirt, tumbling in space. Touchdown is a glancing blow, its resting place a shadow. In the last minutes of its precious battery, it sends back the image of a cliff. My father, too, has gone, his journey passing beyond my knowledge.

Orbiting cameras search for the lander's remnants, revealing the comet's blasted surface in ever clearer detail, its texture like old skin. Near perihelium, it begins to glow. Gasses erupt. Rubble and dust are ejected into space. The very thing that makes it shine is eating it away.

Scattered Across the Stars

J.K. Fulton

The giant puffball fungus, calvatia gigantea, *can reach up to one hundred and fifty centimetres in diameter and weigh up to twenty kilograms. Several trillion spores grow inside the rotting fruiting body, which puff out of cracks in the splitting skin to be blown away by the wind. Only a tiny fraction of spores find suitable conditions to plant themselves and grow – out of trillions and trillions, perhaps one or two. But for the species to thrive, that is all it takes...*

* * *

Cairo, Egypt, June 28ᵗʰ 1911

'I say, Dr Hume, you might be interested in this.'

'Mmm?' prompted William Hume, Director of the Geological Survey of Egypt. His desk was strewn with papers, and the Cairo midday heat lay heavy across his shoulders. Dust motes danced in prismatic shafts of light that forced their way through the blinds. He laid his pen down wearily and dabbed at the back of his neck with a handkerchief. 'What is it, Simpson?'

'A report of fire in the sky yesterday morning, sir, accompanied by loud bangs,' said his assistant. 'Out by el-Nakhla el-Bahariya.'

Hume shrugged and picked up his pen again. 'A meteor. Not exactly uncommon.'

'They're reporting some large fragments on the ground, though.'

'Are they, by Jove?' Hume leapt to his feet. A fire in the sky meant nothing to the geologist. But rocks? Rocks were another matter. 'Arrange a car, Simpson!'

'Yes, sir,' grinned his assistant. He'd hoped the old man would say that. Anything to get out of this cramped stuffy office and interminable geological survey reports.

37

Over a hundred miles along the road towards Alexandria, Simpson began to regret his decision. Hume had brought along a stack of papers and insisted they continue working; Simpson had merely swapped one hot and airless office for a much *smaller* hot and airless office. But still, if it meant he could feel the dirt beneath his feet and carry out some fieldwork – actually get his hands on some rocks for a change – it would be worth it.

'Ah, here we are,' said Hume. 'Right, step lively, Simpson! I want to collect as many fragments as possible. And witness statements, too. I want to know *everything* about these rocks.'

Simpson stepped out of the car into the blazing heat and got to work. There were a dozen fragments at least, spread over an area several miles across. It was a miracle that no one had been injured – no one, that is, apart from a farmer's dog, which had apparently been vaporised instantly. Conveniently leaving no evidence except for the compensation claim from its owner.

Simpson presented the largest meteorite fragment to Hume, who cradled it reverently in his hands.

'What a marvel this is. It has come from across space, Simpson, and now I hold it in my hands,' said Hume in hushed tones. Night had fallen, bringing with it a blessed coolness and a blanket of brilliant stars. 'How far, do you think?' The older man's face was lifted up, and Simpson could see the starlight reflected in his eyes.

'I couldn't say, sir,' said Simpson, following Hume's gaze skywards. But it *was* a marvel. Not that the rock had come across space, but that Hume's gaze was fixed on the stars, and not on the rocks beneath his feet.

* * *

The tardigrade, sometimes known as the water bear, is a micro-animal less than half a millimetre long. It can survive in conditions that would kill most living creatures: temperatures from nearly absolute zero to one

38

hundred and fifty degrees Celsius; pressure from the vacuum of space to six times the pressure at the bottom of the ocean; ionising radiation hundreds of times stronger than the lethal dose for a human; decades without food or water. If it finds itself in conditions that don't support life, it can go dormant ... and wait for the right conditions to come again.

* * *

Leicester, U.K., February 19th 1992

'That doesn't make any sense,' said Miranda, wiping Guinness from her upper lip. The beer garden was freezing, the halo around the moon foreshadowing a sharp frost, so she huddled closer to the patio heater. 'How can a meteorite come from Mars?'

'Big rock hit Mars, rock go boom, bits of Mars thrown into space,' said Gertie.

'Must have been a bloody big rock,' muttered Miranda. 'And knock that words-of-one-syllable shit on the head. Just 'cos you're a post-doc and I'm still struggling to get my thesis done.'

Gertie grinned. 'Best thing is, we think we've seen some biomorphic signs in the rocks. We've been breaking off bits of the Nakhla meteorites and sending them around the world for analysis, and some bods at NASA found something that looked like the paths left by bacteria.'

'Alien bugs?'

'Could be. Or just natural formations. Or maybe even my grandad's cold germs. I told you how my grandad was working in Egypt for old man Hume when they discovered the meteorite?'

Miranda nodded. 'That's probably why you've been obsessed with the mouldy old rocks for so long.'

Gertie glowered. 'But it makes you think, dunnit? I mean, Mars is dead, now, but it wasn't always. What if there was primitive life there? What if there are fossils?'

'Or dormant bacteria. Like in the Siberian permafrost. Or those wotsits, tardigrades.' Miranda frowned. 'What if there are living space bugs in your meteorite?'

Gertie laughed. 'Not likely. That rock was blasted into space by an impact bigger than a hydrogen bomb. Eleven million years floating around our solar system, then *wham!* it slams into Egypt. Can't imagine anything surviving that.'

'But say it could, though,' said Miranda. 'If it could survive that, it could survive anything. A journey from another star, maybe.'

Gertie looked up at the sparkling constellation of Libra. 'Yeah... been thinking the same thing.'

* * *

The zombie ant fungus, ophiocordyceps unilateralis, *is a parasite that modifies the behaviour of its hosts. It takes over the brain of an ant, and drives its host to seek out the perfect position for the fungus to reproduce: the ant locks its jaws to the underside of a leaf, and a stalk of fungus springs from the ant's head, ready to spread its spores and infect another generation of zombie slave ants.*

* * *

BBC Broadcasting House, London, June 6ᵗʰ 2007

INTERVIEWER: We're joined today by Doctor Hari Mistry, from the University of Geneva. Welcome, Doctor Mistry.

MISTRY: Hello. It's nice to be here.

I: So, what can you tell us about this planet you've discovered?

M: Well, it's not just me. It's the whole team at Geneva, especially Professor Gertrude Simpson, who's been the real driving force behind this project. Not forgetting the HARPS crowd in Chile – sorry, that's the High Accuracy Radial Velocity Planet Searcher. So, the star we call

Gliese 581, in the constellation of Libra, has at least three planets. Gliese 581d is the most interesting, 'cos we think it's within its star's habitable zone.

I: So we could live there?

M: (chuckles) No, I doubt that. It's very different from Earth – for a start, its mass is over seven times that of our planet. Its year is only sixty-seven days, and we think it's probably tidally locked, with one side always facing its sun. Anything that lives there would have to be *extremely* hardy.

I: (laughs) So we won't be taking our holidays there?

M: No, but it might have liquid water, which is very exciting. And it's right in our neighbourhood – only about twenty light years away. Luckily, Gliese 581 is fascinating a lot of people right now, not just in the scientific community. Fingers crossed, we'll get some more funding to pursue it.

I: Thank you, Doctor Mistry. Let's hope you get that money!

* * *

Acrobat ants, from the crematogaster *genus, prey on grasshoppers, termites, and even wasps. When an ant finds its prey, it attacks, and releases a spray of pheromones that alert other ants in the vicinity to come and help. When a food source requires several trips, the ants will lay a chemical trail that alerts the entire nest of the prey's location.*

* * *

Transcript of The Extraterrestrial Agenda episode 212, youtube.com, April 2nd 2019.

Hi folks, it's me again, Steve Perspex, with another blistering exposé of the treasonous international extraterrestrial conspiracy. Remember to Like and Subscribe!

So, this week I heard about 'A Message from Earth'. Have you heard about this? So, right, this bunch of 'scientists' get together back in 2009 and say, hey, wouldn't it be *great* if we broadcast our presence to Gliese 581, an alien star system.

What's worse, they opened it up to any idiot with an internet connection. They crowd-sourced the apocalypse, man! They packaged up five hundred and one messages and beamed them from a Ukrainian Space Agency dish – and if that doesn't set off your alarm bells, I don't know what will.

The messages arrive in 2029.

What possessed them? Even guys like David Brin (and you know what I think about him) think this is, like, totally stupid. There's only one explanation – they're *already* under the aliens' control!

It's time to prepare, man. Time to get that bunker stocked. Who knows how long it'll take them to get here?

But I know one thing.

They're coming.

Driving to the moon, with ghosts

Kathleen Bell

I take the wheel of the
black jalopy forgetting
I can't drive.

Even at seventy, it's a long trek.
I wait for air to thin

and the earth spins, showing
beachcombers, mudlarks,
oil aflame, forests, milk-
spun clouds oozing a clear
trickle.

But you're beside, behind me. I feel
safe. Gravity lessens, oxygen slips
away. You don't need breath, and this
past year I've learnt to do without.

It's smooth now, clear, we're joking
about green cheese and men in the moon.
Someone quotes Wells, or Verne,
conjures a simile, a film when it all starts
to go wrong.

Behind me there's a gasp,
hands ease, a mouth fills
up with blood, eyes
close.
Beside me there's a toppling crash

and I'm driving on alone
where tears can't fall here,
in this airless night.

So I drive on (don't mock) and
on
to a hard stillness where
touch endures like the first
footfall more than a
thousand years.

A matter of scale

Simon Fung

Anchored to the riverbed by her boots, Zebie watched as the beasts swam through the pulsating current of the fluid-filled caverns. They were plump things, twice the size of Zebie, with a dimple in their centre. Her *metavitometer* crackled gently as they passed, reading quantum activity six orders of magnitude lower than the limits for sentience. There was no conscious thought in these creatures, their actions dictated largely by chemical gradients. And yet, there was something charming about the way they bumbled along the river. Zebie had logged these creatures in her report as *Feldchar* – 'the generous' in the old language. These creatures swam migratory circuits, gobbling up nutrients in prosperous parts of the caverns, and redistributing them as they swam along. The *Dradmu* – 'wall dwellers' – formed an interlocking network of roots that made the organic walls of the cavern and ate the nutrients released by the Feldchar. The Dradmu's bodies took the strain of the rapid currents, sheltering more fragile creatures that lived behind them.

The metavitometer picked up a clip. Not enough to indicate sentience, but there was something more complex coming along. A *Vlahorn* or 'guardian'. It rolled along the riverbed, towering over the Feldchar. Feelers from the Vlahorn grasped at the Dradmu's root nodules in silent communication. The Vlahorn continued on its way once it had determined that all was well. Zebie held out her hand as it approached. She had been nervous the first time she had encountered one. Although not intelligent, these animals could still be dangerous. A quick scan of the creature had revealed stores of corrosive chemicals packed inside, ready to be released should it encounter anything hostile. Zebie could have shot it apart with her *ablater*, but she was here to observe and document this ecosystem, not destroy it. The Vlahorn reached out and touched Zebie. Its feelers wriggled. Zebie's hand mimicked the root nodule shape Dradmu used for friend. The Vlahorn paused. Then moved on.

It was time to call it a day. Zebie reabsorbed the metavitometer into her abdomen; stored for later use. She deactivated the suction on her boots and swam with the current amongst the Feldchar. Zebie had been cataloguing the lifeforms on this world for seventeen cycles now. Her job had taken her to see many wonders across the universe. Brilliant lights caused by atmospheric ionisation, impossible landscapes carved out by planetary currents, geological histories imprinted into the layers of terrain, but her favourite had to be the planets that contained living ecosystems. On these, creatures performed an intricate dance, and managed to contribute to the stability of the whole, even without conscious thought. Although Zebie's people had explored many worlds, they had yet to find one that contained intelligent lifeforms. It saddened Zebie. Surely, they couldn't be the only ones in such a large universe.

Zebie drew near to one of the exits of the network of caverns. A Vlahorn zipped past her. Purposeful and quick, quite unlike the gentle patrol she had met earlier. Zip. Another. Zebie ejected the scanner from the storage compartment in her abdomen and analysed her immediate environment. The water was thick with *adro*, the chemical produced by the Dradmu when they were afraid. Not afraid, Zebie reminder herself, responding to cues associated with danger. It was unprofessional to project emotions on to other creatures. Zebe latched on to the riverbed by her boots. She cautiously walked forward, extruded two extra arms from her body and drew ablaters from her internal storage so that she was holding four at once. As a rule, she wasn't supposed to disturb the natural order of things, so her weapons were for self-defence. Ahead, Vlahorn piled up, ejecting corrosive substances at an unseen enemy. The Dradmu around her quivered. Then, one by her foot erupted. From its insides, thousands of black creatures poured forth. Zebie yelped and stumbled backward. The creatures darted about, searching for a fresh host. Feldchar, Dradmu, or even Zebie. The creatures swam towards her and she opened fire. High energy bursts disintegrated parasites. But there were too many. She kept firing. She tripped over the limp root of a dead Dradmu. Barbed tips extruded from the black things as they prepared to invade. Was this how it would all end? A Vlahorn came up from behind Zebie, wrapped its body around the cloud of invaders and assaulted them with a battery of corrosive chemicals. A lone invader attached itself to the Vlahorn, but Zebie incinerated it with her ablater before it could burrow into her ally. Zebie signed the gesture for friend and pressed it against the Vlahorn and it responded in kind.

The tide of battle swung in their favour. The invaders had been numerous, but the Vlahorn's tactics, though crude, were effective. The invaders were decimated. Vlahorn still sniffed around the battlefield, searing invaders where they found them. Although Zebie hadn't found any intelligent life, it had been quite the adventure. But now it was time for her to go. She made her way to an exit passage, squeezed past some Dradmu to enter the air chamber. She waited. A mighty gale picked up and she rode it out to where her ship awaited.

***

Bernard sneezed. He had been worried that he'd be too sick to work today but was starting to feel much better. He browsed through the data files being transmitted by the TITAN telescope. A thin atmosphere on planet ENGY3468 but no signs of water so no chance of supporting life. He crossed ENGY3468 off from his list. Bernard sighed. He had always dreamed of finding intelligent life out in the universe. Surely, humans couldn't be the only ones.

STAR

WOMEN

Considering the Stars

Teika Marija Smits

Cassandra woke before dawn. She lay in bed for a while, hoping to return to sleep, yet sleep eluded her. So she sat up and pulled back the brocade curtain of her four-poster bed. Cool air fell onto her face and she smiled as she sensed the stirrings of a new season. Summer had arrived.

Turning to her bedside cabinet, she slid open a drawer and reached for her beloved books, her secret books, which she'd hidden amongst her handkerchiefs. Her Jane Austens and Ann Radcliffes. She could perhaps read a little, and then return to sleep. Yet her restless limbs rebelled and sent her out of bed and to the window.

She drew the curtain and gazed out at the cloudless, dark sky. The stars winked at her, teasing her with their mysteries. She thought of Caroline Herschel and her telescope, and all the wonderful things she had discovered with it. Oh, for a telescope of her own!

Cassandra decided to take a night-time walk. She would venture into the dark, letting it wrap itself about her while she listened to its secrets.

She put a dressing gown over her shift and stepped into her slippers. Leaving her bedroom, she crept along the silent, dark hallway, careful to not wake Mama, who was a light sleeper. She went down the moonlit stairs and crossed the hallway to the parlour. From there, she could slip out to the east garden.

The formal garden, with its looming topiary, was disconcerting, but when she was in the meadow and striding towards the lake, she felt … wonderful. It was good to be outdoors and alone. Free of the confines of propriety and decorum. Free of Mama's concerns over her attire and behaviour, free of her endless sniping about Cassandra's reading habit. A habit which was, in her mother's opinion, inappropriate for young ladies.

Cassandra looked up at the stars, which seemed to share in her joy, threw her arms into the air, spun around and laughed.

What if, one day, someone were to fly out there, like a bird, and unravel the mysteries of that jewelled night-time tapestry? Could such a thing ever occur? She shook her head at her foolish thinking and, coming to the edge of the lake, sat down.

However, she *was* living in extraordinary times. It was as though anything could happen in this new century. Not a month passed without some new invention being dreamt up. There was even talk of instant light, that strange illumination that came from coal gas, being used in London. And since Mary Wollstonecraft's famous thesis, it seemed as though women were everywhere, doing everything. Perhaps it wasn't so wild to think that one day men, and women, would be able to somehow travel to the heavens.

Cassandra gazed at the reflections on the surface of the lake. Here, before her feet, was a liquid sky, and if only she were brave enough, she could bathe amongst the stars.

If only she were brave enough.

But what was there to be fearful of?

She had swum in this lake as a child. Her and her brothers and her beautiful, daring cousin, Henrietta, had spent many a happy summer's day swimming in this lake, their governess gently scolding them for being too boisterous. She had not been afraid then. What was she afraid of now?

Discovery. The unknown.

Yet there was no one about. The servants wouldn't be up for some time, and she couldn't be seen from the house. The weather wasn't inclement, and it was highly unlikely that any creature in the lake would harm her.

Before she could think herself out of her decision, Cassandra took off her dressing gown and shift. She stepped out of her slippers and into the lake, laughing at the shock of the cold water on her skin. It was far from warm but she knew that her body would soon acclimatize. She fully submerged herself, gasping at the cold, and propelled herself through the water. It took a moment or two for her limbs to remember what to do, but soon she was swimming with ease.

The rhythmic movement of her arms and legs brought warmth to her body. Gliding like a Naiad through the fluid black mirror, she watched the ripples of water fracturing the starlight. She was swimming through constellations, an astral traveller.

A splash behind her startled her.

She turned, her heart pounding, to see a pale, moon-like face above the water.

'Nice innit?' said the young woman, as though it were perfectly unremarkable that they should both be here, in the lake, at night-time.

'What are you doing here?' Cassandra demanded. She then blushed, all-too-aware of the unseemly situation she'd found herself in.

'I always come here,' replied the intruder, irritation in her voice. 'Though I'm usually here at dusk. But I was that tired last night I could hardly drag meself into bed.'

The young woman swam to the edge of the lake. Cassandra, abandoning all thoughts of what her mama would say if she saw her now, followed her.

'Never seen you here before,' said the servant girl, her voice more gentle now.

'It's my first time,' said Cassandra. 'I mean, at night-time.'

'Well, don't let me stop you,' said the girl. 'There's water enough for us both.'

The girl took off again and Cassandra trailed after her. Soon they were swimming beside each other, silently back-and-forthing across the starry lake.

After a while Cassandra noticed the horizon beginning to lighten. 'I'd better be going,' she said.

'Lord!' said the girl. 'Me as well.'

Climbing out of the lake they pulled their clothes over their wet bodies, eyes averted, smiles at their lips.

'P'raps see you here again?' said the girl.

'Yes,' said Cassandra. 'I would like that.'

***

When Cassandra crept into the house, her mother met her on the stairs.

'Whatever are you about, child?' she exclaimed. 'And your hair! It's wet!'

'So it is, Mama,' said Cassandra, 'so it is.' And she grinned as she ascended the stairs, the liquid stars dripping to the floor.

Valentina

Mary Byrne

'Good morning, ladies and gentlemen and Councillor Boardman.' The voice of Mr. Bloomfield, the manager, boomed from a stand at the front of the canteen. He'd borrowed a microphone but it wasn't working properly. 'May I welcome you to this special occasion in the history of our little sweet factory.' He was so excited that he spat out as he spoke. 'The beautiful Miss Valentina Tereshkova, the first and only lady to go into space, is gracing the Palatine Rock Company with a visit.'

Valentina, an interpreter called Pavel by her side, smiled and waved.

Everyone cheered. Anne was too scared to join in. Any minute, she would have to present a bouquet of roses. Her sweaty palms gripped the thorny stems.

'Miss Tereshkova flew round the earth forty-eight times over three days. *Three days on her own.* Imagine that. That little body hurtling through the dark.'

They all turned to stare at Valentina. Her chubby cheeks glowed with health and she looked as if she could easily throw Mr. Bloomfield across the room.

'It makes you think, doesn't it, about what you ladies can do if you really set your minds to it.'

The women groaned.

'Miss Tereshkova, as some of you might know, started off in a factory – a cotton mill of all things. But she worked hard – a correspondence course, I believe – and look at her now.'

Anne didn't hear the rest. She realised no one had told her *how* to give the roses. Was she supposed to curtsey like people did on the News when they met the Queen? Should she just hand them over? Say something?

Mr. Bloomfield was gesturing in her direction.

'Come forward, Anne Thornton.'

She stepped out.

'Anne is only just fifteen, our youngest employee *and* a great fan of yours.'

Was she? No one had ever asked, like no one had asked her whether she wanted to do this. She admired Valentina for her bravery but didn't know much else.

'We have specially chosen her for this honour.'

He started clapping and everyone joined in.

She moved towards Valentina and held out the flowers with both hands as if she was a beggar offering. When she glanced up, Valentina was smiling, the interpreter busy whispering.

'Anna,' said Valentina in a strong accent. 'Thank you.'

She felt her face and neck flush. Her heart raced. A moment later, Mr. Bloomfield was leading the visitors towards the work areas. They stopped to put on white coats and caps.

Anne joined the queue of rock-rollers and packers to go back to their positions but as she passed the table, Mr. Bloomfield waved frantically at her.

'Miss Tereshkova,' he hissed, 'Miss Tereshkova wants *you* to show her round.'

'But you're supposed to do that, Mr. Bloomfield.' They all knew he'd had a suit specially made for the occasion and had been practising his speech for months.

'She bloody well wants you.' His eyes bulged. He pulled at his shirt collar.

'I don't know what to say,' said Anne.

'Well, you'll have to work something out pretty damn quick. Apparently, what I say doesn't count.' He stood, gritting his teeth while trying to smile, Councillor Boardman embarrassed beside him.

***

Anne thought she'd better shake hands first. That took a few minutes.

'This way,' she said, showing them into the sugar boiling room.

The sugar boilers – all men – stared, wondering what had happened to their manager. Machines clanked and whirred. The sweet, heavy smell was overwhelming.

She pointed to the big vats. 'The sugar is boiled at two hundred and sixty degrees.'

'Speak up, young lady,' said Pavel. 'We can't hear you.'

So she shouted. The men began to snigger.

'The boiled sugar is thrown onto that.' She pointed to a long marble slab. 'Some of it is dyed pink. It's spun to make it more solid.' She hoped that was the right way round. 'Then it's flattened and the pink and white are cut.'

Valentina nodded as if she knew everything about the process. Anne could feel the sweat running down inside her coat.

A large man was standing patiently by the slab, holding a huge pair of scissors.

'And this,' said Anne, pointing to the man, 'this is Brian who cuts the letters.' It would be alright now. Brian liked her.

Without saying a word, Brian leant over, cut strips of pink and white into letters, then pressed them onto a roll of white sugar lying like a dead pig on the slab. He covered the carcass with a layer of white and another of pink and put it into a rolling machine from which he pulled out strings of rock like long pink snakes.

'Miss Tereshkova would like to know what words you are making,' Pavel said.

Brian nodded to Anne.

'Well.' She knew the answer to this. 'Normally, the rock says "A present from Blackpool".'

The visitors looked puzzled.

'You'll see.'

The women took over. They rolled the rock as it cooled and cut it into individual sticks.

'This is what I do,' said Anne.

'No men?' said Valentina.

'No. Women have smaller hands so it's easier.'

Valentina shook her finger at her. 'And smaller...' She rubbed her thumb against her fingers as if she was counting money.

Who would have thought a Russian would be so straight-talking? Nobody in the factory questioned why the men got more pay.

***

She took them back to the canteen, assuming Mr. Bloomfield would be there, but he had disappeared. A tray of tea things – china cups and saucers and silver-coloured teaspoons – had been left on the counter along with a plate of biscuits.

'You are to have tea in Mr. Bloomfield's office,' said Anne.

'No, here,' said Valentina, pulling out a chair. 'You,' she pointed to Anne and then the tea urn.

'Me make tea?'

It was something she did all weekend at the café, so she might as well. She poured water from the urn into the big metal pot and then into mugs, ignoring the china cups.

Valentina gazed at her as they drank.

'Mama?'

'My mum? She works in a café.' She indicated the tea things. 'Makes tea, food.'

Valentina nodded.

'Papa?'

'No papa.'

The woman put on a sad face. She pressed her hand to her chest. 'No papa.'

Anne had read the local newspaper about the visit. She knew Valentina's father had been killed in the war when she was only two. Valentina was probably thinking the same thing had happened to her dad. She wasn't going to say he'd left when she was at junior school and she could hardly remember what he looked like.

The visitors were whispering together.

'Miss Tereshkova would like to know why you aren't in school.'

'School?' This was a bit cheeky. 'I didn't like it and I was no good.'

They chatted again.

'She wants to know what you do like.'

It had been so long since anyone had asked her, she wasn't sure. Mum hadn't asked her whether she wanted to leave school. It was just assumed she'd get a job, and one of the regulars at the café heard about an opening at Palatine.

'I like ... I like ... I like walking by the sea. I can see the beach from my bedroom window.'

They nodded, expectant.

'I like walking at night when the moon's out and you can see the reflection on the waves.'

Now they were looking worried. She sounded like a freak.

Then she remembered. From a very long time ago when Dad was there, when they didn't live above the café.

'I like dancing,' she said.

Valentina jiggled about in her seat. 'Rock and roll,' she said, emphasising the r's.

'Yes and no.' Anne wasn't likely to ever meet them again and her mother wasn't listening. 'I used to go to ballet lessons. A long time ago. I was quite good. I loved those lessons more than anything.' She paused. 'More than the whole world actually.' It was a ridiculous thing to say to someone who'd gone round the whole world forty-eight times, but when Pavel translated, Valentina put her head back and laughed loudly.

'You dancer,' she said, wiping her eyes.

'Not anymore. I mean lessons cost money.' That was embarrassing so she hurried on. 'But I know all the Russian dancers. I got books from the library: Anna Pavlova, Tamara Karsavina, Galina Ulanova, Natalia Makarova.' She was amazed she could remember the names although she'd probably got the pronunciation wrong. She heard the excitement in her voice like a small child rabbiting on.

'You dance for me?'

'Now?'

'Yes.'

She got up, moved some chairs back, took off her shoes and did an entrechat quatre, followed by a pirouette, as best she could in the white coat. She hadn't forgotten anything.

Valentina clapped her hands. 'Prima ballerina assoluta!'

'Yes! Yes! That's right.'

When Mr. Bloomfield appeared at the door, glaring at her, she didn't mind.

'Thank you, Anne. I'll take over. Please would you be so good as to come to my office,' he said to the visitors. 'You have not talked to Councillor Boardman.'

***

When they were cool and wrapped, Brian gave her a bag with the special sticks of rock. She ran up to the office as they were leaving and handed them to Valentina who pulled one out and stared quizzically. Anne pointed to the message and Pavel explained.

Valentina kissed her on both cheeks.

'Goodbye, Anna. Please dance.' She extended her arms as if she were doing second position.

Mr. Bloomfield grimaced. 'The chauffeur's waiting.'

***

The visit was almost a memory when she got a letter, an official-looking one with a typed envelope. Her mother waited, frowning, until she'd opened it.

'Well?'

'It's from Councillor Boardman. He's sent me...' she looked down at the letter, 'he's sent me ballet lessons!'

'Ballet lessons! Whatever for?'

'Someone asked me what I like.'

Laika

Sarah Doyle

Moscow street-mutt, unloved
stray. Eleven pounds of bone,
of pelt, of tail. Who can weigh
the heart of dog? What dials
or instruments may measure
loyalty; the desire, hard-wired,
to obey? Dogs have no gods,
know only to worship the hand
that feeds. There is no canine
word for *pray*. Brave little
cosmonaut, faithful to a fault;
caught and collared, Earth no
more than a distant ball with
which you cannot play. How
the words that sent you on
your way crackle through
the ragged dishes of your ears,
a comet's tail of breaking
syllables that even now leave
their trail: *Laika, in. Laika, lay.*
Good girl, Laika. Wait. Stay.

Note

Laika: 1957 Soviet space dog, one of the first animals in space and the first to
orbit Earth, she died from overheating. Laika's remains disintegrated along with
her craft, *Sputnik 2*, on re-entering Earth's atmosphere.

What became of the girl who counted

Emma Lee

Starting at the destination, Katherine Johnson worked backwards,
to create a story arc in reverse so it wouldn't break when told in order.

Aged ninety-seven, she was awarded the Presidential Medal of
Freedom.
Even in her wheelchair, she'd travelled further than most.

Everybody was concerned about them getting there.
We were concerned about getting them back.
She created a one-star observation system
to allow Apollo 13 back safely.

Determination of Azimuth Angle at Burnout,
Placing a Satellite Over a Selected Earth Position:
her co-authored paper describing orbital spaceflight
in equations to specify the landing position of the craft.
The first time a woman in the Flight Research Division was credited.

John Glenn told engineers to *Get the Girl*
to double check the computations.
If she says they're good, I'm ready to go.

An early job saw her double-checking an engineer's maths.
Something didn't follow the arc of the radius; a square root error.
Did she question it? A woman questioning a man,
a woman of colour questioning a white man. A deep breath,
Is it possible you could have made a mistake in your formula?

She used the nearest bathroom,
immune to the *whites only* convention;
there was no sign on the door, after all.
She ate at her desk rather than the cafeteria.

Sputnik's launch saw her providing the maths
for the lectures given by engineers
in the Pilotless Aircraft Research Division
and the Flight Research Division,
forming the core of the Space Task Group.

When Katherine's husband died of cancer,
Ella Fitzgerald had played the Mocambo,
opening *George Gershwin's Songbook*, new chapters for both.
In 1953, Katherine worked in the Maneuver Loads Branch,
investigating turbulence and analysing data from tests.
Katherine and her husband moved to Ella's birthplace, Newport News,
the year Ella released *When the Hands of the Clock Pray at Midnight*.

I counted everything. I counted
anything that could be counted, I did.

[Readers are invited to test the theory by reading the poem in reverse]

Pathfinder

Katherine Franklin

Every time I visit New Delhi and look out upon the skyline, the city's architectural endeavours appear more and more magical. Beneath a century's worth of receding smog, towering apartment blocks reach slender fingers towards the hazy stars. In the half light of the growing morning, I can see drones dotting their sides, artificial brains sliding along graceful paths from one plant to the next on the hydroponics panels. A city engineered to breathe. Too complex to exist earlier. Too late to fix anything.

A breath rattles out of my throat and escapes into the air. My knees ache with cold where they press into the damp moss that covers the roof, but I don't move to stretch them. Instead, my fingers worry at the hem of my clothes, tracing the silk's weft.

If the sky were clearer, if the towers hadn't tried so hard to touch the heavens, I might be able to see what my eyes truly seek. A launchpad. A ship. A life coming to an end.

'What you doing up here, Parnaanii?'

A smile crinkles my lips as a small figure topples onto all fours beside me and peers into my face.

'Divya,' There's a tease in my tone that disguises the hoarseness. 'It's well past your bedtime – I should be asking you what you are doing up here.'

My only great-grandchild pouts, her lower lip shining out of a pudgy face. 'You missing your own party. Everyone missing you.'

I laugh, turning to face the sky again. Is it cruel to let my family practice missing me? They will have plenty of time to come to terms with my absence, after all.

'I've never been one for parties,' I say. 'And I wanted to look out over the city one last time.'

'Are you scared?'

I watch Divya try to cross her legs, manoeuvring each by hand, seemingly unaffected by the weight of her question.

'I'm worried, and I haven't got much sleep, but I'm okay.' I can't help imagining the thousand ways I could die during the mission, despite the one sure way I will die regardless.

'Don't worry. I see you when you done.' Divya lets a massive grin seal her eyes tight.

Again, I laugh, and the motion threatens to break into a cough. 'You will be a good deal older by the time anyone will be able to see me again, Divya.' My heart holds me back from telling her that I might fail. If that day comes, a trip to rescue her great-grandmother will be the least of her concerns.

'You see. I be astro-naut like you, Parnaanii, and I save you.'

I move my head close to Divya's ear. 'Well then, little woman, I will see you in the stars. Now let us get you to bed.'

Ignoring Divya's half-hearted protests, I hoist her onto my hip and rise to my feet, swaying a little under her weight. As I carry her down the stairs, I do my best to put thoughts of the coming week out of my mind. My gut knows my last mission will be difficult. But it must be done. For the good of us all.

* * *

Time flits like a shadow from one day to the next. I'm familiar with these routines – and familiarity speeds perception. Patterns become impulses, form routines, embed themselves until they're second nature. Until I'm here, my feet pacing the echoing length of the gantry to the ship, cool air rushing over my bare scalp.

Beautifully butt ugly, the prototype squats atop tonnes of pristine rocket. Humanity has measured our resources and distilled them into this form. The cockpit, once the technicians have bundled me into it, is not much bigger than my own body. Cables snake away beneath flame-retardant fabric panels, plugging into the capsule's most important occupant: the computer.

One of the doctors has followed me and I can see the fine hairs of her eyebrows knitting in concentration as she secures me in my seat, making sure all the cables are aligned properly.

An IV drip stabs into my left arm. I stare at the pressure cuff.

'Okay,' the doctor says. 'We're ready for connection now.'

She reaches behind the back of my head and pulls down a fabric cap, adjusting it, making sure it fits perfectly and aligns as it needs to. Having the electrodes mapped to the right part of my brain is crucial.

'How long until launch?' I ask.

'Two hours,' she replies. 'There'll be long enough to get familiar with her again.'

I smile and close my eyes. I'd known the answer, but this might be the last time I ever talk to another human, face to face.

Then the ship's computer, Skok, presses her interface around my mind and links her learning modules to the areas she's interested in. She settles there like a hangover in reverse – something tingling behind my eyes that promises to expand my awareness rather than limit it.

I don't know whether it's some kind of cybernetic placebo. But when I open my eyes again, I imagine her behind them, analysing the patterns I pick out in the environment around me and adapting them into her own knowledge base.

My heart beats away the seconds until launch.

With precisely eight minutes to go, the arms connecting to the rocket retract. Beneath me, a mountain of raw firepower balanced on the eggshells of careful engineering begins to thrum.

Mission control reads out the times. Sixty seconds. Fifty seconds. Thirty. The numbers pierce my eardrums.

I ready myself for the first kick of thrust, eyes heavenwards, fixed on a point beyond the claustrophobic roof.

When it comes, it's so much worse than I remember. I race away from the world and it presses back on me, determined to keep me in its grasp. But I can't let that happen. The drugs help. As the wall of force crushes my lungs, they ensure some air passes into them.

The noise slips away and the burn abates, leaving me weightless above the dying Earth. Ten billion people are incarcerated upon her surface. I catch my breath, pressing my eyes tight to avoid droplets of sweat. Air flutters along my lungs, tingles at my spine, tickles the sides of my throat. I let the cough spill out and see bright red droplets splatter across my palm.

'Commander, this is Lunar Command. Are you okay up there?'

'I'm fine, thank you, Lunar.' They can tell more from Skok about my physical condition than I know myself. 'How are we looking?'

'We're all set to start the systems test, so you just stay put.'

'Let me know if anything comes up.'

It feels strange, having so little responsibility over my own flight. I should be doing half of these checks myself, or at least helping, but at my age, in my condition ... Safer hands should take the wheel. I remember my old missions with a pang of loss, recall my younger, line-free face. Unfamiliar. As if she will never be me and I was never her.

'Commander, we're having some issues with the data link. We're going to have to put a hold on communications while we figure it out. Please maintain radio silence until we say otherwise.'

I mute my transmissions, automatically searching for a window that doesn't exist. Instead, I close my eyes and frame a question to Skok. As she parses my clumsy question, semi-darkness is replaced by fathomless space. Earth curves into the pitch horizon, atmosphere shrouded with haze, its surface covered in the patchwork grey of mankind's construction. I'm over the daylight side now, and along its circumference I spot a brief dart of fire – one of the supply shuttles come back from the moon or the asteroid mining rigs, no doubt. They're bailing out a ship that has more holes than buckets.

My eyes drift open to the control panel in front of me. Everything reads 'normal' on the faster-than-light drive, but that's just what a team of engineers and scientists say, based on almost no experimental data. My husband used to say it was like making a soufflé blindfolded without a list of ingredients.

My chest tightens. He's down there somewhere, looking up at me in spirit, if not in body. Instead of wondering if he remembers me, I try to imagine the Earth's regeneration. Great stretches of green creep over the landmasses in my mind, clawing back precious leagues like an unstoppable algae. If the FTL drive works, if I can get the data back, if I can survive long enough ... that might just happen.

'Alright, Commander, we have the issue sorted. Ready to proceed with the drive test.'

Reenabling my microphone, I bring up a view of the drive information. 'Ready when you are, Lunar.'

Behind my back lies Earth. Ahead, the stars. The seat and the straps holding me in begin to press into my flesh, juddering under the drive's acceleration.

'Burn underway,' Lunar announces. 'Accelerating to threshold velocity.'

I squeeze my brows together, ready for the jump. I tense my muscles, doing everything I can to stay conscious. I can feel Skok prickling at my awareness. A near-constant stream of measured drugs and hydration fluid pushes into my bloodstream via the IV tube. The bars on the screen monitoring our reserves shrink lower by the second.

'Three seconds until threshold. Five until radio disconnect.'

Metal presses my palms where I squeeze the armrests tight.

'FTL sequence priming. Standby for disconnect.'

I mumble a reply through clenched teeth. 'Come get me when this is done, Lunar.' Divya grins at me in my mind's eye, an image graven on memory's stone.

At the last word, the ship bucks as if we've smashed into a brick wall. The radio fills with static. Blood spikes between my teeth.

Forcing my eyes open, I monitor the screen. A dozen graphs, a constant feed of data logs, all updating in real time. Colour-coded. Chaotic. I scan for patterns or sudden deviations – we need smooth, or at least predictable, lines.

I spot a discrepancy. A swatch of colour denoting the difference between our calculated position and expected flightpath. We're travelling faster than the speed of light through the warped fabric of space, and we're straying from the path. A fraction off could see me whole solar systems adrift. Lost in the void. Plunged into the heart of an improbable star.

I manipulate the controls, coaxing the shifting colours towards stability. Skok lurks in the back of my mind, watching my every movement.

'Five seconds until drive disengages,' I say, more for the company of my own voice.

The navigation error was brief. I hope it's not a fatal half-second.

Four seconds to go now, and I'm reacting on instinct alone. My arm pounds with pain where the IV attaches, punching its drugs into me to keep me functioning. What started as a constant stream has become a stuttering pulse. We're about to run out.

Three seconds. Needles jostle the length of my throat, crowding under my jaw. I cough, gritting my teeth. I have to hold on for two more seconds, concentrate. Bile and blood pushes up my windpipe.

One second.

The drive disengages. Everything on the screen goes haywire in the second of transition. I am pressed back into my seat with a sudden burst of deceleration and thank the stars that we came out of FTL the right way around.

'Where are we?' I ask Skok.

She's calculating the answer. An image of the view outside appears behind my eyes.

We float in the void between solar systems, distant points of light pricking the velvet backdrop. I sense Skok marking out where her paths of investigation lead.

Whatever coldness lurks beyond our capsule's walls burrows into my head. It numbs my thoughts. Our engine splutters, out of fuel, bringing the burn to a close. Freed from pressure, the cough leaps out of my throat. Bubbles of blood tickle my lips.

Skok sends a stimulatory pulse into my neurons to poke me awake. Her calculations finished, she's begun to beam the data back to Earth across the empty sky. From what she can triangulate, we've strayed from our original course but are still within an 'acceptable' margin of error. We were meant to arrive in the middle of a solar system with a potentially habitable planet, but we'll have to content ourselves with being stranded.

I swallow down a lump in my throat. Humanity has what it needs to leave Earth. To give the planet room to recover, as long as they can use the last of their resources wisely enough. Their colony ship won't have the time or fuel to come and rescue me. Not even Divya, with her sweet dreams of reunion.

Skok's transmitting her entire source code back to lunar now – code that will be forever intertwined with my human insight as we lurched through the dark together. It gives me some small comfort that when my family leaves towards a new beginning, a part of my mind will be there to guide them.

A weight settles on my chest. The capsule's interior grows dim.

Still, the lights in my mind stretch across unfamiliar aeons in configurations no other human has set eyes upon. I swallow those strange stars as I slip into unconsciousness.

DYSTOPIAN
SKIES

The Chequered Flag

Tim Bombdog

I am space station
I have rockets in my pockets
Stars in my eyes
While I race to the moon.
Every cell, every molecule
Breathes space dust and follicle
My solar plexus is veined
With interstellar trails
All the way to infinity and beyond.

A galaxy lies within me
But cold wars, hot wars, star wars
Bring satellite shite and space junk.
They bring trouble, they bring pain, they bring strife,
But they bring me to life
As I race through space
With the grace
Of Apollo.

Rings green, reverse matter, and doppelgangers seen
Whilst my spleen is a balled fist of Mysteron.
The black hole of dreams swallows gravity
Without suffocating airlock
No cranes, no platforms, no gantry, no pain.

Its lunar pace dictates
This space race with dark speed
But I am not geostationary, reactionary, revolutionary.
I am white light with squares
No stars, no stripes, no tools, and yet
This space boy is a winner!
Pin me down, without a doubt

Treat me like an alien clown
This space boy is the winner!
Fazer me, when I slow down
For I shall have the final shout
Pop the champagne, raise the prize
This space boy flies the skies!
This space boy flies the skies!

Always Carry A Spare

J.K. Fulton

The last thing you want to hear when you're four light years out from Earth is the emergency alarm.

'Shit shit shit,' said Gilmour, his mouth full of biscuits, crumbs spilling from his lips to catch in his beard.

I clipped my bottle to its magnetic mount and swung myself towards the hatch.

'Shit,' repeated Gilmour, more emphatically. Fifteen months I'd spent cooped up in this tin can with him; fifteen long, dreary months, and every single thing he did annoyed me, from his refusal to shave to his monosyllabic conversation. It was almost nice to have a break from the routine – he'd been into his second hour of complaints about the ship's biscuits when we'd been interrupted by the alarm.

He swam behind me along the tube to the Command Centre. That was a bit of a grand term for another pokey compartment on the good starship *Waverley*. There were two flight chairs, two consoles, two screens. Redundancy is the company's watchword. Always carry a spare.

I pulled myself down into the pilot's chair and strapped in. The console sprang to life, a great big alert splashed across the screen. EMERGENCY REAL SPACE TRANSLATION.

'What's up?' asked Gilmour, settling into the chair in front of the spare console.

'Kill that alarm, would you?'

Gilmour grunted and tapped some keys. The blaring alert stopped. It was like going deaf.

I dismissed the warning message from the screen and brought up the log. It wasn't good news, but it wasn't terminal, either.

'The Z-module's gone,' I said. 'We had to drop out of hyperspace.'

'What do you mean, gone?'

I brought up the diagnostics. 'Just not responding. It happens. They sometimes have these spontaneous failures. That's why we carry a spare.' Without a Z-module, we couldn't navigate hyperspace.

'Fucking creepy things,' said Gilmour. 'Never liked 'em.'

I knew what he meant. Advanced Neural Navigation Module, we're supposed to call them, but no one ever does. To the poor saps who fly these tin cans between the stars, they're Z-modules. Z for Zombie. When you think that the most crucial component of a starship is a severed human head, wiped clean of all memories, and reprogrammed as a navigation system, it *does* creep you out a bit.

'Well, get it going again,' snapped Gilmour. We were in the middle of nowhere, four light years from *anything* in any direction.

'Don't get your knickers in a twist,' I muttered. I brought up the operations manual. Always RTFM. *Always.* No point trying to look clever and missing a step that leaves you drifting in interstellar space with no one but Gilmour for company. 'OK. Looks simple enough. The spare Z-module is all set up. We just need to close the connection to the old one, connect up the new one, then reboot.'

'Reboot?'

'It'll be fine,' I assured him, trying to convince myself at the same time. I scanned through the instructions again. 'OK. Panel 23. Open it up.'

'Why me?'

'Because I'm reading out the instructions.'

He glared at me but unclipped himself and drifted across to the bulkhead.

He popped the panel open, and I heard an exhalation. Probably of relief that there weren't two heads staring out at him. Both Z-modules were safely contained in opaque white plastic cubes. 'What now?'

'Unplug the cable from socket A and plug it into socket B.'

'That's it?'

'The tricky bit is at my end,' I said, looking down the screen. I ran through its diagnostics, and it looked OK. Slight glitches in the navigation matrix, but nothing to worry about. It was probably just an older unit. It didn't surprise me that the company had used a refurbished module as the spare.

Gilmour strapped himself in again. 'Now what?'

'Reboot,' I said, and pushed the button. The lights flickered, the air system stopped hissing for a fraction of a second, and all the electronic hums and whistles cut out ... then everything came back. I let my breath out through my nose, quietly, softly.

'Is that it?'

'Only one way to find out,' I said. 'Engaging hyperdrive.'

* * *

The emergency alarm shrieked, and EMERGENCY REAL SPACE TRANSLATION flashed up on my screen.

'*Shit*,' said Gilmour.

I tapped at my console.

'What's happening?'

'Shut up and let me find out,' I snapped. I brought up the error log, the system events, the diagnostics, and everything else I could think of.

'Well?' asked Gilmour.

'I can't concentrate with you wittering on,' I snarled. 'Go and eat some fucking biscuits.'

'Was only asking,' said Gilmour in a sullen voice, pulling himself out of the chair and drifting off down the tunnel.

It took me an hour, but I cracked it eventually. There was an anomaly in the input buffer. Maybe a random particle of hyperspace radiation, or just a glitch in the sensors. When it hit the neural interface, it caused an overflow that cascaded throughout the whole system, shutting down the Z-module. A one-in-a-billion chance. Unfortunately, because the primary module hadn't finished processing the input buffer, the corrupt data was still there, and destroyed the spare as soon as it tried to navigate into hyperspace.

I explained the situation to Gilmour.

'So you're saying it's your fault?'

'It's no one's fault.'

'You destroyed a perfectly good module by not clearing the buffer before you connected it.'

I glared at him. 'If you'd like to submit a documentation improvement request, I'm sure the company will review it for the next operations manual.'

'Just saying,' said Gilmour belligerently. He was bigger and stronger, and from the way he kept clenching his fist it looked like he fancied taking a swing at me. 'So that's it. We're marooned. Adrift.'

I grinned at him. 'Not quite.'

'What do you mean?'

'We've got a spare for the spare.'

* * *

'Oh Jesus, that's disgusting,' said Gilmour.

I'd cracked open the cold storage unit. *This* spare head wasn't hygienically sealed in a pristine white cube. Its eyes stared blankly ahead, its mouth open in a silent scream. A section of painfully white vertebrae protruded from the ragged red flesh of its neck.

'Pick it up,' I said.

'Why me?'

'Because I'm reading the instructions,' I said, holding up the operations manual datapad.

'Look how well that went last time,' muttered Gilmour.

'Do you *want* to be stuck here forever?'

Gilmour shot me a look, but reached in and picked up the head. 'Hurry up, this thing is freezing.'

'We have to blank and program it,' I said. 'We'll need to open one of the other modules.'

It took us three hours. We opened the primary module, took out the old head, then netted up the new fresh (all right, frozen) head and snapped on the connections. Running the module in initial boot mode wiped any latent memories and patterns from the brain, then formatted it with the navigation software.

Sweat was pooling on Gilmour's face by the time we'd finished. 'Why didn't they provide a whole module? Why just a loose head?'

'Costs,' I said. 'The hardware of a Z-module is expensive. The wetware is cheap.'

'*Cheap*? It's a human head.'

I shrugged. 'They pick them up from the penal colonies for next to nothing,' I said. 'Like you and me.'

'What?'

'What were you in for?'

'Robbery,' muttered Gilmour.

'Not armed, I take it.'

Gilmour shook his head.

'Just as well, or you might have found yourself in our freezer. Rather than enjoying as many ship's biscuits as you can eat.'

'How about you?' asked Gilmour.

'Securities fraud.' I gestured at our less-than-opulent living conditions. 'Did you think anyone would volunteer to crew *these* ships?'

'Never thought about it,' he muttered.

'Let's see how our chilly friend is doing.'

The diagnostics completed, and I scrolled down the screen. Green.

Green. Green.

Then Red.

'Shit,' said Gilmour.

'Shit,' I agreed. The initialisation had failed. The brain was mush. Maybe it had spent too long in the freezer, or maybe there were brain plaques. But this lump of defrosted meat would never get us home.

Gilmour deflated. His belligerence disappeared, and he folded in on himself. I thought he was going to cry.

'So that's it?' he asked at last. 'We're dead?'

I didn't respond.

'No more spares?'

'Well,' I said. He looked at me, a glimmer of hope in his eyes. 'You really think we need *two* people to crew this ship?'

'I don't know what—' His eyes widened as the stunner caught him in the neck, and his limbs jerked spasmodically .

I pondered the best way of slicing through that thick neck.

'Always carry a spare,' I said, as I made the first cut.

Hero of the Soviet Union, Twice
Alexie Leonov's (May 30 1934–October 11 2019) Walk in Space, First
James Walton

A tether of sixteen feet
is the degree of separation
between the escaping ink of forever
walking over the Volga's profile

etched out of a far Gulag
where my father Arkhip
us of Siberian birth
saw the commissars take him,

an enemy of the people.

Like his son, dreaming of circumferences
the hatch too small
without the release of conscience
the sun too bright an enigma.

Five hundred kilometres out
Pavel knocking a spanner's message
to shrink by valve released
those first steps over Crimea,

weightless before all accusation.

To return within a capsule
painted as it was by forest fire
grim as a cell's silence.
My family's boots all lit up,

such small small steps
for a cosmonaut
nothing below or above
as the ash settled,

about our release.

The Pioneer's Dilemma

Yevgeny Salisbury

`<Did you invent this?>`

Messages from Earth were usually longer. Darkon carefully rearranged a few things on his desk, lining up the pencil, the notepad, the photo of the Second Generation Explorer he was meant to be dating. Was it love? Hard to say...

Hell, this message from Earth was concerning.

'Kiz,' he said and his colleague looked up. 'Come and have a look at this. Reply concerning the Lo-3. I'm just a bit...'

'The Lo-3? Is it eight years already?'

'Yes, but can you see why I'm concerned?'

She leant over his shoulder a moment. 'They've taken it badly, do you think? They're touchy about fertility on Earth, I told you.'

'They shouldn't impute a value judgement, but that does say to me I've overstepped what they think I should be...' He flung up a hand and sighed. He supposed in a way he hated lying to them.

'I said it was a risk.'

'I know. But we can't string them along forever.'

'So you keep saying, but we've managed so far. Every probe they've sent ... and they've all been such easy hacks. And every update you've sent ... until...' She patted his shoulder. 'Just sort it out, Darkon. Make it look like a simple logical step from all the files about Earth.'

'It kinda was.'

'Well, there you go.'

'It'd have been unethical not to send it, Kiz. They could be dying in their millions waiting for us to get this place set up. If they're never coming, we had to give them other options.'

'You mean *you* had to.'

'Kiz, even with dampening we're cleverer than almost all of them.'

She shrugged and went back to her desk.

'Psycho,' he muttered.

'I heard that.'

'Yeah, yeah.' He looked towards the window. It was a pleasant, sunny day. He wondered how it was on Earth. They never said, but why would they? 'I'm going for a walk,' he said. 'I've got to think.'

'Tune-up and answer now,' said Kiz.

He shook his head and headed for the stairs. Sure they would expect an immediate response, but he'd take the chance that after eight and a half years, they wouldn't actually be counting the minutes.

He sat down on the grass, beneath a tree, and watched a fledgling bird being fed. A Lo-3 for birds would put a stop to most of that; the majority of them just wouldn't feel the urge to reproduce. They wouldn't be unhappy about it. Problem solved, had the problem been too many birds.

Except it wasn't, and the birds were beautiful. Everything was idyllic. Everyone had worked hard: on the planet, on themselves. He looked at his hands. Indistinguishable from human hands. It hadn't been part of the brief. Not at all. But there's artistry in terraforming. To really get it, you must live it. Love it. The humans would love this place. And he hated lying to them.

Hue of Blue

Rebekah Tobias

I am luminescent, iridescent
in the cloudless morn.
Let me stay, gaze awhile,
as you face the trial of the day.
I'm malevolent, benevolent, dragging tides of tears.
I am Izanami,
Sina, Selene, Gwaten, Anahita.
I am Chandra, resolving, revolving, unveiling the invisible.
For once
I was your destination
The goal of every dominant nation.
Sputnik, Soyuz, Gemini, Apollo.
Fruit flies, wine flies, macaque and frog
Flew through silence; returned to you.
Finally, you came: small stepping onto Tranquility's sea.
Mankind's giant leap in a crater of discovery.
You dug, you drove, you leapt, and then
you left me behind.
As I dance in your orbit
I'm still here, in the hue
of the blue, watching you.

Mother

Paul Rudman

The light is within me; I am the divine.
The light is within me; I am the divine.
The light...

'Where's Mummy?'

K tried to turn his head, to look out of the time-freezer, to find the voice. The sound came from his right. He tried hard, but his head wouldn't move.

Frozen time on a long voyage does this to you; the body shuts down for minutes on end, occasionally bursting into brief slow-motion life, like a prisoner, spirits buoyed by visiting time.

'Please mister, can you find my mummy?'

That voice again. This time, K turned enough to look sideways through the freezer's carbon-glass skin. Nothing. Just the next device, its occupant leaping from one moment of resurrected life to the next, patiently waiting to complete her self-imposed sentence.

K closed his eyes. His master had told him to expect hallucinations, to wait until his head cleared before forcing his way out. He must follow the advice. He took a slow, deep, breath, and returned to the mantra.

The light is within me; I am the divine.
The light is within me; I am the divine.
The light is within me; I am the divine.

Deep breath.

It is time.

There was little space to move inside the time-freezer. The window wrapped his head in a futile attempt to stem the claustrophobia in the minutes before and after stasis – the settling and rousing times. Only by twisting his head awkwardly around and down could he see what he was doing. He reached into a hidden pocket inside his gown and pulled out a small explosive hammer, the metal end pointed and heavy. He tried to position the hammer in the corner of the window, its weakest point, but twisting his body in the small chamber was like trying to dance in a straitjacket. The hammer slipped from his grasp.

His heart missed a beat as the hammer landed on a lower left rib. Then, relief. For a moment he imagined its charge igniting, the pain as the central pin shot out, through skin, bone, flesh. There would be enough force to send the metal right through his body.

His hands trembled as he picked up the hammer and slowly placed it against the carbon-glass composite. Then, taking it back a short distance, he made a sharp blow against the window. The shockwave passed through him, and for a moment he was disoriented, seemingly somewhere else – the training ground, Tuesday morning practice, kinetic weapons. A feeling of dread came over him. He would fail the exam a third time, he was sure. He would be punished again. Then, his mind was back inside the freezer – shards of glass, a chemical smell, and silence. There was no going back now. He sat up, and looked around the dimly lit, windowless deck.

Ninety-nine stasis chambers. Superstitious idiots. Everything in nines. Pathetic. Bathshi has no numbers. We, the believers, are the divine. We shall prevail. My master was right. To find one's purpose in life is the ultimate joy.

K smiled.

Ninety-eight to purge and this life will be complete.

He climbed down onto the deck and walked over to the next freezer. A bearded man, late twenties. Silk gown with gold trimmings, buttons gently pulsing with golden light. Beside his head, the hologram of a young woman.

They take everything, these Centralists. Our land, our women, our happiness. No wonder he's so rich. But we shall prevail. We know the truth. We have the light.

He sat down on the deck beside the freezer and began to examine a small window of flickering lights and touch buttons. Regular glass. No explosive charge required, just a well-aimed hammer. One blow, and the hatch cover shattered.

Shutting down the chamber was easy, its demise already present – a virus, introduced in manufacture, waiting to be activated. He keyed in the pre-arranged sequence. One last button to press.

'The light is within me; I cleanse the darkness.'

Pressed.

No more resurrections for this unbeliever.

Next time-freezer. A young woman. Spiral hair. Semi-transparent gown. Beside her head, the hologram of a bearded man – the body in the first device.

Sad that such beauty hides an inner darkness, the blackness born of rejecting the truth, the darkness without Bathshi. My master saved me from the darkness, rescued the child-me, after...

K couldn't bring himself to remember that day, the last day of childhood innocence, when warmth became fire, father became silent, and mother was taken. Only K was left. K, and a few memories: a mother's eyes looking into his, a father who would make everything right, memories kindling love and loss in equal measure. And now, revenge.

He pressed the buttons.

They're together now, in the light of Bathshi.

K worked his way along the deck, each freezer in turn. Nothing would stop him.

The light is within me; I am the divine.

His master's mantra. Ten thousand years of spiritual growth. The focus of life. The ultimate answer.

Halfway through now; halfway to perfection.

He paused to look into the next chamber. An older woman, black gown and tied-back silver hair.

Something familiar about this woman.

K shook himself.

Concentrate. Must stay focussed.

Deep breath.

The light is within me; I am the divine.

He knelt down to the glass maintenance hatch, fumbling in his gown for the hammer.

'Help me.'

The child's voice again.

He spun around. Nobody there.

'Who is it?'

He stood up, looking intently around the ship's deck. Ninety-nine time-freezers, forty-nine asleep, forty-nine purged. Nobody else. He looked again at the woman in the chamber as she waited for her life to end.

I must still be hallucinating. Maybe a bug in the virus code that woke me early. Everything's fine. Everything's fine.

K knelt back down, but his body was shaking. He aimed the hammer and struck, missing the glass and denting the casing. He tried again, this time a piece of glass made a small cut in the back of his hand. He stared at his hand, watching as the blood seeped out. Words came to him from his training.

You are the instrument of Bathshi. You are the honoured chosen one.

Instinctively he licked the cut. The taste brought more memories, the end of childhood. Did blood always herald an ending? He took a deep breath. He must hurry. He tried to focus on the control panel. It suddenly seemed more complicated. Slowly, methodically, he pushed the sequence he had learned.

One last button; one less insult to Bathshi.

He shouted, 'The light is within me; I cleanse the darkness.'

'Mummy!'

K spun round, pressing a random button on the panel.

That's no hallucination. It must be a stowaway. I'll find him and send him with the others.

***

It is possible to dream in a stasis chamber. Not in the silence of stasis. Not in the brief glimmers of life that keep the silence from becoming absolute. No, the dreams of stasis come in the wakening, in the journey back to life. Months of unheard emotions, made conscious in the final minutes.

Mia dreamed of playing on the beach with her sister, piling up the white sand into magical shapes, building her own world. The deep rumble of the ocean surrounded her. Her mother waited nearby, quietly watching, with a love Mia would never find again.

Slowly, the scene grew dark. The sand became the slowly undulating surface inside her stasis chamber, the rumble, that of the ship's star drive. She was awake.

Awake! We must be there!

Joy overwhelmed Mia, like the seventh wave. A new civilisation, a new start. She had never felt so happy, so complete. To find one's purpose in life is the ultimate joy. She thought of her sister in the next freezer, her friends, the high priest in freezer ninety-nine; she would see them all in just a few minutes time. A surge of excitement shivered through her body.

We are here. The centre of the galaxy. Our new home with the Great Mother. The Grand Prayer; it is time:

I praise you Great Mother, for creating me.

I praise you Great Mother, for both my parents.

I praise you Great Mother, for the earth, air and water.

I praise you Great Mother, for the four winds.

I praise you Great Mother, for your five graces.

I praise you Great Mother, for your six promises.

I praise you Great Mother, for the seven sacred souls.

I praise you Great Mother, for the eight thoughts of your creation.

I praise you Great Mother, for your nine perfections.

Slowly, silently, the chamber lid opened.

***

K walked purposefully down the row of time-freezers, looking carefully all around, until he reached his broken capsule at the end. No child. He walked back, past the freezer with the older woman, to the far end of the deck, examining everything carefully. Nothing.

Ghosts of unbelievers. Bathshi rejects them all, leaves them to wander for eternity.

He walked back to attend to the next freezer, pulling the hammer from his robe.

'What happened?'

More ghosts.

K ignored the voice, leant down and aimed the hammer.

'What are you doing?'

A hand touched his shoulder. He fell backwards, dropping the hammer, and looked up – into familiar green eyes. Twenty years disappeared. He climbed to his feet and embraced the woman who was taken from him what felt like yesterday. Everything would be alright.

'Mummy,' he cried.

The woman gently rocked him from side to side.

'It's ok. It's ok. Everything's alright. Tell me, what have you done?'

'I did it for you, Mummy.'

'What did you do?'

'I sent them away.'

'Where?'

'Back to the darkness.'

The woman's eyes filled with tears.

'You killed them.'

'They were never alive. They were not of Bathshi; there was no light.'

K felt a warm glow in the side of his neck. The happiness of belonging. The soft redness of Mother.

***

Mia was trembling inside.

Make it real, Mia, to show fear is death.

The shard of glass was cutting her hand, taking the life-force from all it touched.

Forty-nine martyrs. A heavy price to pay, and only one denier to pay it.

Mia remembered tales of the deniers, how they rejected the Great Mother, knew nothing of the sacred numbers, opposed the settlement of planets close to the divine centre of the universe, how they destroyed any connection to the central divine. She hadn't seen how anyone could be so deranged. Now, she understood. Fully.

It is a truth taught to all children of the Great Mother. Every soul has a purpose. One day, that purpose will show itself. She had wondered about that day so many times; when, where, what she would be called upon to do. Never did she imagine this. Alone with the enemy, to save a ship of souls.

She must act. Decisively. For all the Great Mother's children.

She counted to nine, and pressed the glass shard into his neck.

Yet, she couldn't bring herself to cut the vein. There was something about him. Something she couldn't place.

K took a step back. He put a hand to the side of his neck, feeling the blood. He looked at the woman, at the red glass in her hand, the tears in her eyes. She seemed frozen in time.

'Who are you?' she asked.

'We are the light, join us. Bathshi...'

'Mandy...' she pushed past him and pressed herself to the glass cover.

He turned to stand beside her. She didn't notice as he took the glass shard from her hand.

'Great Mother, take this, your daughter, to your perfection, that she may rest with the sacred souls,' she cried out. Then she was on top of him, her hands around his throat. He tried to speak, but only meaningless noises escaped.

For a moment she thought she saw something in his eyes, maybe some sense of regret. In that moment, the glass struck.

And then she was on her own, trying to stop the blood, trying to stand, feeling light-headed, faint. Somewhere, a man was crying.

Mia's last moments were on the deck, beside the control panel of her sister's freezer. She knew this panel, but couldn't think, what did the lights mean? Those colours. As she lost consciousness, she just had time to smile. The panel had been set to run a diagnostic; the failure light wasn't true. There would be only two dead bodies when they reached the colonies. A life for a life.

'Great Mother, take this, your daughter, to...'

About the Authors

Deborah Tyler-Bennett is a European author of eight volumes and chapbooks of poetry, and three volumes of linked short stories. She has been published internationally and has had her work broadcast on Radio Bucharest. Her current volumes of poetry and stories – both King's England Press (2017) – are *Mr Bowlly Regrets: Poems* and *Brand New Beat* (stories set in the 1960s). Her next volume, *Ken Dodd Takes a Holiday*, is forthcoming from King's England.

Emma Lee's publications include *The Significance of a Dress* (Arachne, 2020) and *Ghosts in the Desert* (IDP, 2015). She co-edited *Over Land, Over Sea* (Five Leaves, UK, 2015), is Poetry Reviews Editor for *The Blue Nib*, reviews for magazines and blogs at http://emmalee1.wordpress.com

James Walton was a librarian, a farm labourer, and mostly a public sector union official. He is published in many anthologies, journals, and newspapers. His poetry collections include *The Leviathan's Apprentice* (Strzelecki's Lover Press, 2015), *Walking Through Fences* (2018), *Unstill Mosaics* (Busybird Publishing, 2019), and *Abandoned Soliloquies* (Uncollected Press, 2019).

James Worrad lives in Leicester, England. He shares a house with two cats and another writer. In 2011 James attended Clarion Writers' Workshop, San Diego. His space opera series, *Feral Space*, is published by Castrum Press. He's had fiction appear with Daily Science Fiction, Flurb, Newcon Press and Obverse Books.

J.K. Fulton lives in Leicester, but grew up at lighthouses on the Scottish coast. His stories have appeared in *Shoreline of Infinity* (2016), *Leicester Writes Short Story Prize Anthology* (2018), and *Best of British Science Fiction 2018* (Newcon Press, 2019). His children's books include *The Wreck of the Argyll* (Cargo Publishing, 2015) and *The Beast on the Broch* (Cranachan Publishing, 2016).

Katherine Franklin has been writing fiction since the age of eight but spends most of her time these days writing code instead. Despite (and perhaps because of) having a physics degree to draw upon, she prefers writing the softer, fantastical side of science fiction.

Kathleen Bell is a poet and fiction writer who recently stopped teaching in the Creative Writing department at De Montfort University. Her publications include *at the memory exchange* (Oystercatcher, 2014) and she co-edited the anthology *Over Land, Over Sea: poems for those seeking refuge* (Five Leaves, 2015).

Mark Goodwin was born in Oxford, on January 23rd 1969. Ten months later he was being brought up on a farm in South Leicestershire. There are various ways in which he is transported by the moon – seeing its pale blue hull from a mountain top on an icy winter day is one of his favourites.

Mary Byrne has had short stories published and won the Leicester Writes Short Story Prize 2019 and was shortlisted for the H.E. Bates Short Story Prize 2020. She is currently working on more stories and a novel. Mary worked in a Blackpool Rock factory as a teenager.

Michele Witthaus comes to poetry from a journalistic background. Her first collection, 'From a Sheltered Place' draws on emotions and insights related to the Covid-19 lockdown and was published in August 2020 by Wild Pressed Books. She also has poems in a variety of anthologies and other publications. She is a member of Leicester Writers' Club.

Paul Rudman has been interested in Psychology since his first degree in the 1990s. He is an active member of the Speculators writing group in Leicester and has had 10 stories published since his first in 2016. His stories explore unusual psychological states. Paul is currently working on a novel-length thriller as a vehicle to discuss the role of the unconscious in our behaviour.

Rebekah Tobias was born in Manchester and moved to the East

Midlands when she trained to be a teacher. She discovered the world through teaching overseas in places as diverse as Addis Ababa and Vienna. Happily married, she is mum to an assorted collection of children and grandson.

Richard Urwin is a semi-retired embedded software engineer. When he's not writing speculative fiction, he is playing role-playing games or programming microcontrollers. He might get back into hill-walking if he can find any flat hills. He had a non-fiction book on Artificial Intelligence published by Arcturus in 2016.

Rob Bray lives and writes in Leicestershire. A member of Leicester Writers' Club, he has had work published in *The Best of East Midlands Writing* anthology and a story shortlisted in the Aurora short story competition (2017). He is currently enmeshed in volume two of a historical fiction trilogy.

Rod Duncan is a novelist, screenwriter, photographer and lecturer in creative writing at De Montfort University. His debut novel *Backlash* (Pocket Books) was shortlisted for the 2003 New Blood Dagger and in 2014, his novel *The Bullet-Catcher's Daughter* (Angry Robot) was shortlisted for the Philip K. Dick Award.

Sarah Doyle is widely placed and published, winning the WoLF poetry competition and Brexit in Poetry 2019, and being runner-up in the Keats-Shelley Poetry Prize 2019. She was highly commended in the Ginkgo Prize for Ecopoetry and in the Forward Prizes 2018. Sarah is currently researching a PhD in meteorological poetry at Birmingham City University.

Simon Fung is a scientist by day and a writer on Wednesdays, mostly. He should probably stop saying he's new to writing, because he's been saying that for the last few years. His writing has appeared in *Shoreline of Infinity* (2020) and the *Leicester Writes Short Story Prize Anthology* (2018).

Teika Marija Smits is a mother, writer, artist and editor. Her writing has appeared in various places including *Mslexia*, *Literary Mama*, *Reckoning*, *Shoreline of Infinity* (2019) and *Best of British Science Fiction 2018* (Newcon Press, 2019). She's looking forward to having her debut poetry pamphlet 'Russian Doll' published by Indigo Dreams Publishing this year. She is delighted by the fact that Teika means 'fairy tale' in Latvian. https://marijasmits.wordpress.com

Tim Bombdog (Bomdog) is Leicester's very own post punk poet combining hard hitting revolutionary poetry with a mix of sentimentality, wit and humour. He is a rare poet whose work is rooted in a certain time and place, but is challenging, unique, and of interest to all.

Yevgeny Salisbury grew up on the isle of Anglesey in a cottage insulated by books. He has a degree in Fine Arts and has had poetry and short stories published in a number of anthologies. He is currently writing a novel and collaborating on a musical.

Publishing Credits

+1 by **James Worrad** has been previously published by *Daily Science Fiction* (January 26, 2012).

A short history of a universe in fold theory by **James Walton** has been previously published in *Punk Noir Magazine* (August 5, 2019).

'Driving to the moon, with ghosts' by **Kathleen Bell** has been previously published in *Litter* (Leafe Press, 2010).

'Laika' by **Sarah Doyle** has been previously published on the Keats-Shelley Memorial Association's website, in *The Keats-Shelley Review* (Routledge, 2020), and in *Wordland 8: Time We Left* (Exaggerated Press, 2020).

'Neil Armstrong's Three Stage Punctuation' by **James Walton** has been previously published on Silver Birch Press' website (March 22, 2015) and in *The Leviathan's Apprentice* (Strzelecki's Lover Press, 2015).

'Yuri Gagarin in Dublin' by **Deborah Tyler-Bennett** has been previously published in *Iota 63* (2003).

Lightning Source UK Ltd.
Milton Keynes UK
UKHW040929241022
410996UK00001B/84